Book of Lost Houses: The Second Coming

By Carla Hollar (House Varich), Christopher Howard (House Scathach), Dee McKinney (House Daiereann), Krister M. Michl (House Aesin) and Peter Woodworth (House Beaumayn)

Credits

Written by: Carla Hollar (House Varich), Christopher Howard (House Scathach), Dee McKinney (House Daiereann), Krister M. Michl (House Aesin) and Peter Woodworth (House Beaumayn)

Additional Material by: Adrian Simmons (House Scathach)

Developed by: Nicky Rea and Jackie Cassada

Edited By: Jeanée Ledoux

Art Direction: Richard Thomas

Layout and Typesetting: Ron Thompson

Art: Mike Chaney, Christopher Howard, Aaron Siddell and Drew Tucker

What is Arthaus? It's White Wolf's newest imprint. White Wolf's mission has always been to create *art that entertains*; White Wolf Arthaus is the embodiment of this ideal. Modeled after small press, the Arthaus team strives to create those games and projects that are new, experimental and unique. White Wolf Arthaus now manages whole game lines, supports others and creates specialty projects whenever possible.

735 PARK NORTH BLVD.
SUITE 128
CLARKSTON, GA 30021
USA

Book of Lost Houses: The Second Coming

Contents

INTRODUCTION

We who are old, old and gay,
O so old!
Thousands of years, thousands of years,
If all were told:

Give to these children, new from the world,
Silence and love;
And the long dew-dropping hours of the night,
And the stars above:
—W. B. Yeats, "A Faery Song"

In 1969, a sudden implosion of Glamour brought about by the moon landing burst open the doors to Arcadia for a brief, glittering moment in time. Sidhe from eight of Arcadia's noble houses, banned from Earth since the Shattering, arrived in force and claimed their right to rule fae society. Resistance from the commoners who had managed to survive without their sidhe overlords for six hundred years led to the Accordance War, a bloody five-year conflict that ended with the arrival of a young Gwydion sidhe named David Ardry. Possessing the sword Caliburn and receiving the blessing of a great chimerical grey griffin, David Ardry brought an end to the war by negotiating a series of accords between the warring parties. The Kingdom of Concordia, corresponding to the continent of North America in the Autumn realms, became an example of tolerance and cooperation between sidhe and commoner, with David Ardry occupying the throne of High King for nearly three decades.

In 1998, David Ardry disappeared. Caliburn chose an eshu storyteller to carry it in search of the missing king. With no ruler to guarantee the stability of the realm, Concordia dissolved into a land on the edge of war.

Not long afterward, sparked by events that shook the supernatural realms, creatures from darker realms of the Dreaming made their way into the world of mortal flesh.

Banished for centuries for their actions during the ancient battle known as the War of Trees, Dark-kin found the Autumn realms once more accessible to them—albeit with some difficulty. These Denizens have had varying degrees of success integrating themselves into their new existence, making alliances here and there with some of the Kithain, reviving old enmities or forging new paths for themselves in a world grown exceedingly alien to them. Their arrival presaged a new phase in the great pageant of fae society.

Relations between commoners and sidhe continued to worsen as the twentieth century came to a close. Now Concordia lies broken, torn apart by the ravages of a war that threatens to expand to the other lands of the fae. David Ardry's realized dream of peace and unity among fae has splintered into warring factions. Nobles and commoners eye one another with wariness, remembering past injustices and envisioning future ones. Fae prophets and soothsayers search their dreams for signs of the future. All omens point to one outcome: Ahead lies Winter.

A new kind of Glamour spreads throughout the realm; it is born from suppressed dreams of revenge and the reawakening of ancient grudges, spawned by the presence of strange Dark-kin who change the nature of the Dreaming by their very existence in the Autumn realm. The gates between the worlds weaken once again. Those houses left behind in 1969 now find the ways open to them. By choice, by compulsion or by mishap, a second wave of noble houses gains entrance to the world of flesh.

Who are these newcomers and why have they chosen this moment in the history of the fae on Earth to return? What purpose does their arrival serve? Does their arrival signal a new phase in changeling politics?

The answers lie within the pages of this book, a compilation of documents from each returning house. For the first time since the Shattering drove them from the realms of their fading Dreamers, these newly returned houses reveal their histories, legends, customs, beliefs and plans for their uncertain future.

How to Use This Book

Book of Lost Houses: The Second Coming presents a look at some of the houses that remained behind in Arcadia when the first wave of sidhe returned to the Autumn realm. The first Resurgence consisted of fae from the five Seelie houses of Dougal, Eiluned, Fiona, Gwydion and Liam as well as the three Unseelie houses of Ailil, Balor and Leanhaun. For three decades, the

Seelie fae have held the reins of power throughout Concordia and most of the fae realms in other parts of the world. With the Second Coming, the balance swings to a more equal position. Three more Unseelie houses along with a single Seelie representative level the playing field, with one house—Scathach, with its dubious nobles—holding the balance of power in its grasp.

With the arrival of these new and unexpected factions, new realms of possibility have opened up for the sidhe. Bringing with them old ideas, these returning houses confront a society wracked by war and in need of strong leaders.

Though the Mists prevent most of these new houses from remembering exactly why they have traveled to the Autumn realms, they know one thing. Something has happened in Arcadia to force them back into a world that they left six centuries ago. Nothing happens without a reason, and the arrival of houses known for their warriors and prophets seems to indicate that momentous events loom in the future of the fae.

Unlike the members of the houses who have made the world of humans their home for the past three decades, these newcomers retain a sense of dread, a carryover from their recent experiences in Arcadia and en route through the Mists. The dark times are coming, their arrival seems to say. The harbingers of Endless Winter have arrived. In their Dream-built prisons, the Fomorians stir, gathering together their savage dreams and lavishing their attention on the need to escape from their bonds. Filled with endless hatred for their captors, these ancient foes of the Tuatha de Danaan and their descendants—today's changelings—quicken in their slumber. Soon, the omens whisper, they will awaken.

The houses that have recently fled Arcadia know this, at least for now. Perhaps the Mists will eventually cloud their memories, but now the sense of urgency drives the new houses to seize any opportunity they can to make their concerns known to the fae already ensconced in the halls of power. And if those fae do not listen, many feel they have the right to seize power and *make* them heed these dire warnings.

In the meantime, however, the new houses that have made their way to Concordia find themselves caught in the midst of a war. They seek leaders so that they may observe the formalities dictated by fae protocol and find only an empty throne and several warring factions, each in support of a preferred heir. Why then, they ask, should we not put forth our own candidates? Do we not bring news that shakes the very foundation of fae society? Can we afford the time to play through these petty succession wars? And if we do, will we emerge the stronger for it or end as a wretched, beaten force incapable of standing against our ancient foes? Are our titles acknowledged to hold as great a claim as those who arrived so many years ago? Will we be accorded our rightful places and given freeholds to rule? What will we do if we cannot claim such shelter? Will the members of our houses become wanderers without a place to call their own? Is our coming the hope these noble houses need to end their bickering? Will our values and beliefs force the commoners to acknowledge the sidhe as their rightful rulers, or does our presence drive them to greater efforts of rebellion? All these things the recent returnees ask themselves. In many cases, there are as yet no answers for them, and they become more impatient and suspicious with each day that passes without resolution. Will they bring even more warfare to a reeling Concordia or the healing the kingdom needs? Fate reveals her tapestry in her own time and at a place of her choosing, but the clock is ticking and Endless Winter looms on the horizon.

This supplement to **Changeling: The Dreaming** provides players and Storytellers with information about the "other" noble houses. Beginning with a fiction piece that embodies the theme of each house, each chapter proceeds to describe the house history, traditions and specialties as well as detailing a few notable individuals and special Treasures associated with the houses.

Contents

House Beaumayn: Crusaders by Destiny Doomed presents a tragic tale of a house divided, betrayed and imprisoned in Arcadia, forced to sit in idleness while great changes took place around it. Finally allowed enough freedom to leave the homeland of the fae, these warriors and prophets have returned with a vengeance, bringing with them a passionate belief that strikes terror into the hearts of those who learn their secrets.

House Aesin: Guardians of the North describes the fae of the icy northern lands. Before the Shattering, these lofty nobles of Scandinavia ruled a world of harsh beauty and stark dreams. Now, though some have returned to their place of origin, others have found themselves cast into the midst of a Concordia at war.

House Daireann: Seasons of Blood details a house favored in war and knowledgeable in the ways of healing—and harming. Holding their enemies as close to their bosoms as their lovers, these hardy sidhe weigh the advantages and disadvantages of their new situation and work to place themselves in the best possible place to attain their goals.

House Varich: Patterns in Sunlight and Shadow tells the tale of nobles forced to leave not only their beloved motherland, but also the elemental spirits over whom they exercised power and from whom they drew their greatest devotion. The land of the firebird and the endless taiga now welcomes back its true rulers. Yet some members of this house now wander a troubled new land known as Concordia, searching for their own dreams of power and sovereignty.

House Scathach: Restless Shadows reveals the details of a house that calls into question the true meaning of nobility. The members' decision to remain behind when the other houses left the Autumn realms in the wake of the Shattering led them to mingle their fate with that of humanity, forging something more than human, less than sidhe. Now, however, other Scathach have returned from the Dreaming to confront members of their house whom they have not seen for centuries.

The **Appendix** offers a selection of ready-made characters from these new houses. Play them as designed or alter them to suit your own concept.

HOUSE BEAUMAYN: CRUSADERS BY DESTINY DOOMED

"Thank you!" he says. You don't thank the Fates,
dreamkin! Ahahahaha! Heeee! We haven't helped you! Your
troubles are only just beginning!
　　—The Hecateae, *Sandman #2*

Prophecies Long Past

To: <Names withheld>

From: <Sender withheld>

Subject: Household History

Brendan here. Included are the long-awaited reconstructed scans of the text of the Marvejols Script. I'm very pleased with the quality of the reproductions, considering the amount of translation it took to work this into modern English. Everything else was re-created as authentically as possible, however, so what you see is what you'd actually be looking at, provided you could read archaic French, that is. Remember to send thanks to Dame Lillian next time you see her; without her efforts, it'd still be under a hill in France, and we'd all be missing a vital part of our own history. It's hard enough to do what we do even with these words, but without them, life would be simply unbearable. So read, learn, enjoy, and remember where we came from and why we're here.

— Count Brendan Beaumayn

We who have always been began in glorious times, when the realms were still hot from the fires of the forge and the world itself could be shaped by little more than imagination. Even in the early days, word spread far and wide of the rise of Gwydion the Grey and his band of noble warriors, who brought order and justice to lands where there were none. On one of the very first journeys Gwydion and his entourage made, they came across a village of mortals slaughtering another village, putting women and children to the sword and burning the buildings of their enemies with whole families trapped inside. What amazed Gwydion, though, was that a sidhe warrior was watching the destruction from a nearby hilltop, weeping as though his heart would burst and yet making no effort to stop the carnage. Thinking him a coward, Gwydion's band made to ride past him and save who they could, but at the sound of their approach the young noble sprang to his feet and blocked their path.

Gwydion was outraged. "What manner of warrior do you call yourself, that you can watch the slaughter of innocents and yet do nothing but weep?"

At this, the young sidhe drew himself up nobly, his eyes flashing with light like twin moons rising over a haunted moor, his words ringing with distant thunder. "I am the warrior Jalendrel, strange lord, and I am no coward, but weep only for the knowledge that it was destined to be thus." He raised his blade, and the assembled nobles saw that one of his hands was twisted and blackened, as if by flame. "Know this: Neither you nor I nor any of your knights may change that, on the pain of my life, else the greater evil be served."

"What greater evil is there than the deaths of innocents, while warriors stand by and do nothing?" Gwydion asked.

"The greater evil, strange lord," responded Jalendrel, neither voice nor sword wavering before the mightiest sidhe the world had yet seen, "is that a good man should act at all, if he knows his actions would serve only to advance a wicked design further."

Before the puzzled lord could respond, a terrible monster leapt out of the flames of the burning village, its ancient lair at last uncovered by the destruction around it. Roaring fire and dripping poison from its jaws, the ferocious creature began striking down attackers and defenders alike in its rage. Gwydion and his followers fell back, dazzled, but Jalendrel prepared and averted his eyes in time. He then fell upon the monster with equally savage fury, wielding his great sword one handed as he hacked into the beast's stony hide. Round and round they dueled, with blood spilling from both combatants, but in the end the young warrior prevailed and slew the monster with a final, tremendous thrust through its heart.

At once, the fascination that had fallen over Gwydion and his soldiers was broken, and they gave a cry of triumph as they rushed to Jalendrel's side. Their joy was muted, however, when they found him weeping once more. "You have slain the beast, noble sir, and for that you should be proud, for if you had not lain in wait for it as you did, a monster such as that one would have taken ten thousand innocent lives rather than just the population of this humble village."

Jalendrel raised his head at this, and the sunset light of his eyes washed over Gwydion in a wave of grief. Yet his words were calm and measured as he replied, "That is true, strange lord, but the folk of this humble village were my kin. If others have been saved by my actions, I must carry to my death the knowledge that my family's lives were the coin this victory was paid in. The future has always been my curse," he whispered, "for though I see what must come to pass, with that ability comes the knowledge that I am sometimes powerless to stop things from happening so." Mustering the last of his will, he raised his blackened hand. "I tried once before, and earned this for my folly, for it was not the destined time to slay the beast, and I knew it." With that, he slipped to the ground, mingling his essence with the blood and ashes.

Moved by such devotion to duty, Gwydion summoned his greatest healers, who used their magic to restore the noble young warrior to health; only his hand, burned by the fire of the beast long ago, could not be saved. Gwydion welcomed his company, and in time Jalendrel the Good Handed became one of the greatest knights of the age, renowned not only for his courage and strength at arms, but also his compassion for the common folk, mortal and fae. When he at last passed into the Dreaming, a shower of stars fell from the sky in homage, and blue flowers bloomed where they blasted the earth away. To this day, it is said among the wise peoples of the world that when the blue flowers bloom once more, Jalendrel will rise again and lead his house against the evils his prophecies foretold long ago.

The Sundering

Like the nobles of House Liam, whose lands we frequently shared, we grew attached to the mortals around us, as much in tribute to the regard Jalendrel had given them as our own fascination with their preciousness. Our reputation among the faerie waxed as well. We were known as great seers, more trustworthy than the snakes of Eiluned. Our skills in the field were valued as well. Whenever the knights of Gwydion rode into battle, you would find members of our house charging by their side. So when the Sundering arrived and the First Crusade soon followed, it was only natural that our highest nobles asked leave of House Gwydion to go with our mortal allies on their quest, in hopes of finding some help for the faerie realms as well. Since we had long served the Shining Host with great distinction, and the lords and ladies of the fae courts proved eager to remedy the spread of Banality, our request was granted. Duke Geremin's force was seen off with much ceremony and celebration, but it was the last time our house would be gathered. . . . until our trial.

The Shattering

House Beaumayn was further devastated when an oathcircle of Harbingers of Exodus were discovered while returning from a small outpost near Antioch in the Holy Land. They bore a load of cold iron weapons and scrolls inscribed with many hideous rituals involving faerie sacrifice and other foul practices; the names in their wicked books included some of the highest of our house. Accordingly, a great tribunal of the faerie lords was called and our entire house put on trial. They accused half of the house of condoning these hideous experiments and the other half of covering the tracks of their kin while they committed their dark deeds. What could be done? Our lips were sealed by the oath of the brothers, so we accepted their insults and condemnations in stoic silence. They would not understand the agony it was to watch as our brothers went mad at their iron forges, the pain of doing battle with our own kin even as we fought the minions of evil without, and so they judged us all guilty of the crimes of a few.

The judgment for our treason is thus: the nobles are to be imprisoned in the dungeons of Arcadia, and the commoners who stood by us are condemned to death. So heinous have our crimes been judged that our standard is to be stricken from all halls, and a great ritual known as the Caul of Silence has been enacted by the Eiluned, removing all memory of our existence from the minds of those outside Arcadia's gates. We have been given a season—under guard—to set our affairs right, and then we will be marched to our waiting cells, there to remain indefinitely. I can hear the dark ones laughing. . . .

We have given them nothing but the truth, and they reward us with oblivion.

Geremin's Heresy

As you may have noticed, there's a significant omission in the manuscript—namely, the original text of the legend of Duke Geremin. Good news: We actually *do* have the original text of the legend. Bad news: Unfortunately for everyone concerned, the pages have deteriorated badly, much worse than the rest of the manuscript. Given the fragile and fragmentary nature of the pages, I didn't want to expose them to the scanner, so I've enclosed a summary below. Read it carefully, though, because it goes to the heart of our House's feud.

Duke Geremin was a popular leader at the time of the First Crusade. Unlike many members of our house, he was charismatic and outgoing and a brave warrior, passionate lover and cunning courtier all at once. During the Crusade, Duke Geremin fell in love with Zubaidah, an eshu princess. Their love was cut short with a cold iron blade, however, and the duke went mad with grief after her death, descending into deep depression and uttering horrible prophecies to any who would listen, until one night when he simply disappeared. Accusations of a murderous conspiracy began to circulate in his absence, and the eshu caliphate had no choice but to heed the will of their subjects and declare war on the Beaumayn host in their midst, leaving only a few survivors to return with the tale. But that is not quite the end of the tale—not yet.

Two hundred years later, Duke Geremin reappeared in the household of two sidhe brothers, the highest lords of our house at the time. Swearing them to secrecy, he told the brothers his tale. Consumed by grief, he had wandered until finally he found himself at the edge of a strange realm, a grey trail winding through a silver forest, where a blinding light as if from a rising sun came through the trees. While he watched, Zubaidah came out of the light, smiling broadly. After a moment it became obvious that neither could cross the threshold of the land, and the Duke pleaded with her to explain what had happened, how she had escaped the iron's curse. In reply she told him that iron is not the end of our souls; as the essence of everything we oppose, iron burns away the impurities we acquire through our contact with the human world, leaving only our true faerie nature behind to begin a new journey.

She then told him that he must find the Iron Road, the path she traveled to reach that forest, and guard it, for it is the one way that will always offer true passage here. Second, she said that as its painfulness increases, fewer will take the iron willingly, so he was to gather those of his line who were worthy and train them in special rites so that they would be able to show others the way and give the worthy the release of paradise. Duke Geremin told the brothers that they must not speak of this to anyone not of our blood, for, as with all the futures we speak of, none would believe us until it came to pass, and in the meantime we would be hunted and abused.

If his instructions were not undertaken, the duke warned, the Dreaming would continue to wither and weaken until there came a time when a dark star shone in the sky. Under its light, the Fomorians would rise from the depths of the Dreaming once again, send the host of the Thallain before them and sweep the Kithain from the Earth and into the chill oblivion of Winter. So saying, he pulled a cold iron knife and killed himself, a contented smile on his face.

The Brothers' War

Even *there* it doesn't end. The two brothers immediately began to argue over what Geremin had told them. The younger held that it was all in keeping with the increasingly dark nature of the visions that house members were receiving, and that it was a matter of blood loyalty that they should carry out a hero's last request. The elder was suspicious of such a neat tale of paradise and believed that sinister forces were trying to manipulate their visionary gifts into bringing disaster on the Dreaming. Before long the argument fell into outright hostility as each tried to convince the other of the rightness of his actions, and soon the house was split into two factions. Both sides were still bound by their vow of secrecy from revealing the heresy to those outside the house, however, and so they began a shadow war instead, pitting kin against kin in a struggle that lasted until the time of the Shattering.

Imprisonment

The manuscript ends there, presumably because the author hid it before the sentence was carried out. It's not a really big problem, though; all of us remember our imprisonment only too well. Shame. Anger. Isolation. Helplessness like nothing you've ever known. Oh, we were treated well—we were still sidhe, after all—but cozy prisoners are prisoners just the same. So while the world turned and the ages rose and fell, we remained the same, pacing our cells and muttering our portents to ourselves. The injustice of being caged while the real enemies of the Dreaming walked free scarred many of us deeply, but we endured. We kept hope alive by planning for the day when we would be called to duty once more. We knew it would come and dreaded and anticipated it all at once, for we knew all too well that the price of our freedom would be high indeed for the fae.

The Resurgence

During the Resurgence, we watched helplessly as the Arcadians sent the other houses back to Earth, ostensibly to combat the spread of Banality, but in fact because their ship of paradise was sinking and they sought to bail out as much as they could. Meanwhile, the cause of that Dreaming's sickness, namely the stirring of the slumbering Fomorians, continued on because the Arcadians could not bring themselves to admit that they had been wrong. They sent the others with little more than hazy pride and ill-defined goals, and we could do nothing but watch, sick with anger and despair, as they nobly went back to the world and fought the wrong fight. Those were the worst years of all the centuries of imprisonment — the years we spent listening to their confused cries and smelling the smoke of their useless wars.

Jalendrel's Code

• *Honor the Future and remember its secrets.*

Ignoring our gifts of prophecy is denying what you are. You must honor and record all your visions and omens, no matter how terrible they may be, and warn others of our house when you see dire events on the horizon.

• *Do not burden others with the Future, lest it break them.*

Many others think knowledge of the future would solve all their problems, but the truth is that it usually only makes them worse. After all, do you *really* want to know whether you and your love are meant to be, or what day you're going to die? Others are seldom ready for all the consequences accepting a prophecy entails. Do not share your visions to those not of our house unless there is great need to do so.

• *Accept your destiny and leave others to theirs.*

This applies to both the good and the bad we see; while we must fight to change what we can, there are some visions even we cannot alter, some events too great for one fae to master. When the future is in your grasp, learning when *not* to act is as important as learning when to take action, if not more so.

Dark Star Ascendant?

Just before the century's end, word came of the light of a dark star and the return of the Thallain, and not even the Arcadians could deny that such news foretold the imminent return of their ancient enemies, just as we predicted it would. Not that we were shown any gratitude, of course—as one, we were brought before the lords and ladies and given a new charge. We were to travel back to Earth and battle the Thallain and other agents of the Fomorians wherever we found them, to bring unity to the Seelie forces and weed out the agents of true corruption from the Unseelie ranks. They said that upon completing these deeds, we would clear the name of House Beaumayn at last. They acted as though they were doing us a great favor instead of simply using us as the cannon fodder against the enemies they themselves were unwilling to face. So saying, they freed us from our chains and sent us back to the waking world, all the while acting as if we were their champions instead of their chattel.

But that's beside the point, really. Just as we knew the Fomorians would return one day, so too did we know we'd be the ones called to lead the charge. It might very well destroy us, but as Jalendrel came to understand with his own village, we must accept that cost if it means destroying the greater evil. So it was foretold; so shall we uphold!

Society

Apologetic warrior, chalk one up for the visitors
Casting fearsome light into the shadows of midnight—
To the underground we descend
With our whole generation to defend
—O. C. Supertones, "Unite"

It is often very difficult for us to get along in modern fae society—there have been so many changes since our imprisonment! The mortal world alone is intimidating, though I'm here as proof that these strange devices can be conquered (if not always completely understood). It doesn't get much easier when you add that to the fact that we represent the return of a house long ago disgraced and stripped of its rights, even of the memory of its existence. Still, we endure because we must.

The Beaumayn Blazon

Unseen for all the time of our imprisonment, our blazon depicts a purple star against a black background. Though not correct according to the later heraldic customs, our house blazon was created before such laws became the rule. Thus, our unusual blazon depicts our house quite well, as we ourselves exist outside the fae norms. This dark star is both our beacon and our burden, calling us to witness the coming of Endless Winter and to battle those who bring it to the Autumn World and the Dreaming.

The Seelie Court

It would be nice if the Seelie Court members made more of an effort to understand us rather than simply pointing their fingers and bringing up the tribunal every time we show our standard. Of those who can cast off the Caul of Silence and remember that we exist, most don't seem to grasp our history very well. If anything, we were *too* Seelie in the old days, not the reverse. We held our tongues because we knew it was the only way we could properly serve our lords, not because we wished to keep anything from them. A thin line, I admit, but still, there's one part about the equation that they never quite understood, no matter how hard they might have tried: *They don't see what we see.* If they did, even for just one day, they wouldn't be so quick to judge us. Instead, they come to us for counsel expecting a glimpse of the future to solve all of their problems, then get angry or turn deaf ears to our words when we tell them exactly what does lie in store. It's so frustrating!

But the Seelie have to be saved from themselves if the Kithain are to survive the Winter, and we've been chosen as the ones to do it. Never forget that. No one says it's going to be easy, or even that we'll survive to see the outcome; there are some things even our greatest oracles cannot predict, after all. But we must do it just the same, though it cost us everything. It is our way.

The Unseelie Court

Few of our house pledge allegiance to the Unseelie Court, and most of those who do only join its ranks temporarily, usually as the result of a fit of depression brought on by a particularly troubling vision. Others may succumb to their Unseelie nature in reaction to the jests and persecution of other houses, letting their bitterness get the better of their judgment. Some others fall when they realize that the future is not only disturbing but inevitable as well. A few—very, *very few*—embrace their Unseelie nature willingly, using their talent for divination to gain advantage in everything from finance to warfare, sometimes even selling their skills to those willing to pay handsomely for a glimpse of their future. They are a small minority, though, and a hunted one as well; we do not tolerate those who would abuse mortals and abandon their duties to the Dreaming.

The Shadow Court

We alone never doubted its existence for a moment, for we saw its shadows swirling around the foulest deeds in Kithain history long before the other houses even knew of the Shadow Court, but as has happened too often in our history, no one listened to us. We did what we could to root it out and destroy it wherever we could, but ultimately we were forced to watch as the Shadow Court steadily grew in power, reaching its claws into everything from mortal wars to Kithain politics. Worse still, we saw its master plan unfolding—the release of their Fomorian allies—and still could do nothing to stop it. The Shadow Court was simply too big for us to fight alone, and the few other fae we did manage to convince of its existence weren't enough to stem the tide. I'm ashamed to admit to such a failure, but in our defense, we did all we could. At least now more of the other nobles seem willing to believe that the Court exists and is a real threat, rather than just a puppet counsel presiding over every Samhain. If only they would act!

Factions

The vast majority of the house emulates Brandell, the elder brother, in following the Code of Jalendrel. We believe that our gifts of prophecy should be guarded carefully lest they be abused by those who don't understand, and we offer guidance only when we feel our audience is ready to accept the consequences of that knowledge. The current chaos is the work of sinister forces seeking to divide the Kithain so that they are easy prey when the Fomorians cross back into this world. We do our best to bring harmony and understanding to embattled fae on all sides of the conflict, as well as to banish the dark creatures of the Dreaming wherever we find them. Above all, we strive to uphold the Escheat and the Seelie Court, cleanse the ranks of the Unseelie, do battle with the forces of the Shadow Court and guide all fae to a new, unified Spring.

Harbingers of Exodus

Some of our benighted kin follow the teachings of Markesh, the younger brother, who taught the heresy of Duke Geremin as gospel to all the fae of our house (and some others as well, I'm ashamed to admit). Under the leadership of Lord Vandermere, their main goals seem to be to locate and map out the lost Iron Road trod, then to reconstruct the rituals of cold iron that will allow them to set faerie souls on the path of the Exodus they seek. They are supremely dangerous enemies, for they share our gifts for prophecy, remember much of the time before the Shattering, and, most terrifyingly of all, they have few qualms about using cold iron on their enemies, since they see it as granting "salvation" to the target's soul! Remember, though, that we are still bound by the ancient oath of the brothers to keep this conflict within our house alone; the Harbingers are our problem, and we must deal with them on our own.

It is also important to note that while the few of our house who choose to remain Unseelie make up a number of the Harbingers' ranks, most of its members are all too Seelie in their outlook. They truly believe they are doing what must be done to save the fae race, and if the means they must employ seem hideous, it's only because the truth is usually hard to endure. Twisted logic, yes, but their logic just the same. Remember that before you cast them all as wicked, heartless villains.

House Boon

All members of House Beaumayn are natural prophets—glimpses of possible futures regularly come to them during dreams and meditation. These visions are often quite cryptic, although the changeling may attempt to decipher them with a successful Intelligence + Gremayre roll (difficulty 8). Remember, however, that no matter how well understood they might be, they are still only *possible* futures and may not necessarily come to pass. Obviously, these prophecies are the province of the Storyteller, who decides both when and how they appear. When in dire need, however, the Beaumayn may attempt to "bring on" a vision by meditating for several minutes, spending a Willpower point and rolling her Glamour against a difficulty of 11 minus her Remembrance score. One must be careful not to invoke this Boon too often in this fashion, however, or else the threads of probability become tangled, the Dreaming is upset and the visions the character receives become increasingly inaccurate, perhaps even dangerously so!

In addition, due to their relatively fresh memories of Arcadia and their imprisonment, all Beaumayn sidhe receive Remembrance 1 for free during character creation.

House Flaw

The unswerving dedication and gifts of prophecy of House Beaumayn have long been a thorn in the side of the Shadow Court and its dark masters. Now with the return of the Fomorians so perilously close to success, the efforts of House Beaumayn pose a bigger threat than ever. Worse, Shadow Court members, those creatures of darkness, can sense the fires of the dark star that burn within house members. Thallain and Shadow Court fae can generally sense when Beaumayn nobles are in the area (Perception + Kenning, difficulty 7), which naturally leads to all sorts of conflicts and story hooks. This doesn't mean they can automatically detect hidden or invisible Beaumayn nobles. Nor should they all try to maul the character on sight—after all, some of the most sadistic methods of inflicting harm are mental or emotional—but they *will* do their best to make the Beaumayn's life miserable once they discover her identity.

Additionally, because of the infamy surrounding their imprisonment, when their true lineage is known Beaumayn sidhe suffer a +2 difficulty on all Social rolls with sidhe of houses other than Liam or Fiona.

Merits and Flaws

Here are some merits and flaws of members of House Beaumayn. While not absolutely exclusive to Beaumayn sidhe, these traits so define the house that Storytellers should consider carefully before allowing any other fae to possess them.

Psychological

Fortune's Fool (4-Point Flaw)

All House Beaumayn sidhe must bear the weight of future events; a character with this Flaw, however, believes for one reason or another that she cannot affect the futures she sees. She might think it is a judgment from her particular deity, believe in predestination, or simply be a very fatalistic soul, but whatever the reason, she believes that events she sees in her visions are inevitable and cannot bring herself to act in ways that would alter their outcome. After all, what's the point? Even if a vision is later proved false, the character simply rationalizes it somehow (*I must have seen it wrong*) or even believes that some greater misfortune will befall her or the others responsible for "interfering" with the true course of events.

Any actions whose success might directly lead to contradicting a vision the character has had are at +2 difficulty, and actually initiating a plan to prevent a foreseen occurrence requires the Beaumayn to spend a point of Willpower

Supernatural

Melody of Days to Come (2-Point Merit/3-Point Flaw)

A character with this Merit has an affinity for a particular type of vision and finds it easier to receive auguries related to such subjects. This affinity is typically a particular theme, emotion or event, although a certain person or persons close to the character are also possible with the Storyteller's permission. One sidhe might constantly see visions of future battles, another could dream of romances yet to come, and so on. All difficulties to consciously "bring on" such omens are at -2 difficulty (minimum 3), and in general they will occur more often than other types of visions. This Merit may be purchased only once without express Storyteller permission—it is very rare to have such control over precognition, let alone specialization.

When this affinity is taken as a Flaw, the character receives no bonuses for bringing on visions and must also choose a specific motif. However, she can receive visions regarding that particular object or theme *only*, thus narrowing the scope of her gift considerably.

Burning Gaze (3-Point Merit)

Beaumayn with this Merit are especially attuned to the presence of their ancient enemies, the Thallain, and can even detect members of the Unseelie Houses or minions of the Shadow Court with close enough scrutiny. The character must concentrate for a turn, then make a Perception + Gremayre roll (difficulty 6 for Thallain, 8 for Unseelie House or Shadow Court fae). Success means the Beaumayn sees such fae for who they truly are. This Merit may even detect those fae if they are hidden or disguised, although the character must score more successes than the hidden character and must succeed at a difficulty 1 point higher than normal. While this Merit is active, the character's eyes burn with the purple fire of the dark star, a sure giveaway for those who know the mark of this house.

Other Common Merits/Flaws

Several Merits and Flaws seem particularly suited to characters from House Beaumayn. These are the following: Art Affinity (Soothsay), Bard's Tongue, Iron Resistance (Harbingers of Exodus), Geas, Code of Honor (Jalendrel's Code), Dark Fate, Higher Purpose, Enemy, Concentration, Nightmares, and Eidetic Memory.

Oaths of House Beaumayn

Like all sidhe, we take our oaths very seriously; unrepentant oath breakers are run from the house without delay. Given our unique gifts, it's not surprising that we have some unique oaths as well, known only to members of this house and those who swear service to it.

Oath of the Dark Star

This day I swear loyalty to the Book and the Blade, to the future that is my destiny, the present that is my duty and the past that is my treasure. I swear loyalty to the members and goals of House Beaumayn, and may the dreams of the damned haunt my mind should I ever break this trust. As the dark star burns above, so does my heart burn in service to thee.

Unlike most others of our kind, both sidhe and commoners swear the same oath upon joining the house— in the eyes of the future, all are the same. Those who willingly betray this oath immediately gain the Flaw of Nightmares, which lasts for twice as long as they served the house.

Oath of the Foretelling

As the Dreaming is my witness, so shall I speak the truth of what I see and nothing else. I shall not close my eyes to any image, nor bend any sound to suit my ears, nor twist my words to shape anything other than the entire truth. May the flames of the dark star consume me if my account is anything but pure.

Obviously, this oath was designed to convince skeptical audiences that a Beaumayn is speaking truly, and it is now traditionally sworn before imparting any important visions to others. A character swearing this oath regains 1 point of Willpower but suffers 2 unsoakable levels of lethal damage if it is broken. Additionally, the chimerical tattoo of a dark purple star appears on the offender's forehead, clearly visible, and remains there until some great atonement is made.

Fostering

Our fosterage is painfully short these days, and the actual fostering process is fairly straightforward—none of this fighting and riddling of the other houses for us. We know our children by the touch of the future on them, and so the newcomer is asked to share all dreams, visions and other omens they've received in their lives. If their blood is true, at least one of these centered around a dark star, always one they feel is significant enough to mention, and that's all the proof we need. After that, new house members swear an oath of loyalty and are told about house history, Geremin's Heresy, the Caul of Silence, the Brother's War and anything else their tutor feels they need to know. Simple but effective in these lean times.

Relations with Other Houses

Most of the other sidhe don't remember us very well yet, which is probably for the best, because if they're anything like their ancestors (and I'll bet they are), it's not going to be pleasant when they do.

House Gwydion

House Gwydion members treats us worse than any of the other houses when they uncover us, and that hurts much more because they used to be so close to us. We were the voices who guided their proclamations, the blades that guarded their backs in battle, and what thanks did we get? Never mind that half of our house submitted to their justice willingly, even helped track down our own kin because we knew it was the right thing to do. We didn't tell them the secrets they weren't ready for or betray our own kin fast enough, and for those "crimes" we were labeled traitors and thrown in the deepest dungeons they could find. I wish I could say we got some satisfaction when they in turn were exiled, but we couldn't. True to our blood, we knew it was just one more step of the dark design that's close to overwhelming both worlds. Why couldn't they have just listened to us before?

Hurt their pride and they'll hurt you *bad*, and that's all there is to it with these tarnished monarchs. Someday maybe they'll come to their senses and remember why Gwydion the Grey once counted Jalendrel the Good Handed as his closest lieutenant, but until then, avoid them. They're nothing but trouble.

House Liam

Our poor cousins have suffered so much, and not a little for the devotion they demonstrated toward us during our time of need. If there's anything the other houses really hate, it's being shown up, and their grace and compassion went a long way to doing that when everyone else had their High Inquisitor's robes on and were ready to start a big Beaumayn bonfire. After we were gone, there was no one left to stand up for them and, well, you've seen what the others did to them in our absence. We have to wake up our cousins, tear the Caul of Silence and remind them of the greatness they used to embody; maybe then they'll reassume their rightful place as the conscience of the Shining Host. Avenge the slights that are done to them as best you can and always aid them when they call—we owe them no less.

House Eiluned

The Gwydion respected us, and that was fine, but these sorcerers always seemed a little *too* friendly, if you know what I mean. They didn't like it when the same circles that turned them away welcomed us. They could never seem to accept the fact that our prophetic abilities are an inherited trait and not some kind of hidden Art. More than once they tried to pry our "secret" from us with wine or warfare. If they knew what they were *really* asking for, though, they would have turned even whiter than normal and vanished that instant. Just because you *can* see the future doesn't mean that you *want* to, especially when you can't always control your "gift."

House Fiona

These fearless lovers and warriors also shared our lands in ancient times and were long the opposite side to our coin: Where we were brooding and intense, they were merry and foolhardy; while we spoke prophecy, they matched us with poetry. They never heeded our advice and loved the battle itself more than fighting the real enemies behind their troubles. Still, they never cared a whit for what the other houses thought of us, and they alone stood with Liam in our defense, despite the objections of the others. They also did well by the commoners in their domain, a tradition they keep alive even today. When they returned they took over most of our old lands and managed them well, and for that we owe them our gratitude.

House Dougal

When our house was brought to the tribunal, no one in House Dougal lifted a finger in our defense. Then again, when it was time to reach a verdict, none of the Dougal delegation voted to convict us, either, so I don't really know what to think of them. They also seem to do fairly well by the commoners in their lands, which is good, and their ethic is very similar to our own in many ways (though I doubt they'd see the similarity as well as we do). I just hope they stick their heads out of their workshops every once in a while and see what's going on in the world around them, before the kinds of machines they love so much knock down the walls for them.

House Scathach

We've always desired a certain kinship with this house; their nomadic ways are much like our own, and their stoicism in the face of the other houses' displeasure is an example we would do well to learn from. Their own abilities with prophesy would seem to link us as well, were it not for their constant attempts to thwart what fate decrees. At the same time, though, our wanderings always have a destination in mind, no matter how unclear, whereas the knights of Scathach seem to wander simply for the feel of the road under their feet. That's fun for a while, but eventually you must choose some purpose or fate will find one for you, and believe me, you want to take the first option if you can.

The Other Houses

We have watched the return of the Unseelie Houses (like we watched the rise of the Fomorians) with a mixture of sorrowful resignation and building fury—sorrow for the miserable wretches of House Leanhaun, who are trapped in their evils by their ancient curse, and fury for the bastards of Ailil and Balor, who are little better than serpents and rabid dogs, respectively. They have all long been deep in the intrigues of the Shadow Court, and if you meet one you would do well to remember our ancient enmity. Their memories are not nearly as bad as those of their Seelie cousins, and few of them would have a problem with planting a blade in your chest if it suits their fancy to do so. Fortunately for us, we have no problem returning the favor, if need be.

We also have hazier memories of other Unseelie Houses that returned from the Dreaming around the same time we did and have since scattered around the world in an attempt to hide from the Seelie Houses and strike up pacts with their Fomorian masters. Thanks to our imprisonment, we know little of them, save that they are wicked to the core and seek nothing less than the destruction of the Seelie Court we hold dear. Unless different facts come to light, that knowledge alone is enough to make them our enemies. Be careful around any strange sidhe you come across, and if it is one of these fellow new arrivals, learn what you can, then report back to the rest of us. If the Shadow Court has new puppets, we must discover whatever we can about them as soon as possible.

Views on Other Kith

Commoners have always been close to our hearts. We've never been the largest house, for one thing, and if you know anything about the First Crusade, you know it was more of a peasants' mobilization than a force of knights and nobles; its faerie counterpart was little different. Our visions of the future showed us early on that mistreating the common kith would only lead to disaster, even if we couldn't convince the other sidhe to follow suit.

Unfortunately, the discovery of the Harbingers of Exodus and their plans to begin the genocide with the commoner kith poisoned the minds of many commoners against us, and I can't say that I blame them for that. The current hostilities between nobles and commoners make this an even more dangerous time for us to reappear. Still, we left behind a lot of friends and lovers when we went to our punishment, and some of them still remember those bonds, even if the Caul of Silence has kept most fae from recognizing us.

Boggans

The heart and soul of the common kith, they were close to forgiving us when we were imprisoned, and more than a few have welcomed us back so far, especially in the Old Country. We didn't unburden the worst of our visions on others back then and we still don't now, but that doesn't mean we can't find peace sipping some hot cider before an open fire and sharing our other worries with a sympathetic ear. Just watch out for the Unseelie ones, though; they haven't forgiven us by far, and they're the ones who will smile to your face while they slip poison in your drink.

Eshu

Just thinking about our history with the eshu makes my heart ache. We began as the closest of allies and respected their system of titles and prestige even while the other sidhe looked down on them as little more than desert barbarians. We still have a lot in common with them—a love of story and travel, a deep sense of destiny and a strong sense of honor. Yet the circumstances that surrounded Zubaidah's death and Duke Geremin's disappearance haunt us to this day. They held us responsible not only for her murder but of the actions of the other fae during the crusades that followed, especially as they became increasingly bloody and useless over time. The eshu determined back then to make it blood for blood, starting with ours, and, barring some miracle, among those who remember us, that won't change much.

Nockers

We don't have much business with nockers; we are beings of prophecy, principle and honor, while they are workers of sweat and grease. They are very similar to the sidhe of House Dougal in outlook and attitude, and generally you should treat them the same way, except be ready to make a *lot* more allowances for their colorful language and impatient manners. Those heretical members of our house who have created cold iron weapons to use in their insane attacks learned their skills from the nockers, which makes us somewhat nervous around them. Still, as Dame Lillian has very ably proved, they sometimes come up with the most amazing ideas, and we know they're basically a good kith at heart—just don't expect them to ever wear it on their sleeve.

Piskies

All I've seen of this kith comes from meeting Delphine. It would seem that they are a cross between the eshu and the boggans with a mischievous dose of kleptomania mixed in. I'd love to see if this holds true of all of them or if she is just a unique case, but so far, so good!

Pooka

We speak of the future, and no one listens; pooka tell the truth, and no one believes them. See any similarities there? They also do a lot to protect children and animals, and that earns even more respect from us. They see the evil falling over the world and do their best to fight it, in their own way. All in all, pooka are a very underestimated kith, even by themselves. Approach them openly and let them know you share the sadness in their hearts, and you'll never find a truer friend.

Redcaps

These dark faeries have never paid attention to anything more than the sound of clashing metal and the cries of the anguished, let alone given thought to the future. They actively avoid examining the consequences of their actions in favor of relishing the moment (or meat) at hand, and that makes them even more repugnant to us. We do not provoke them, however, but simply avoid them for the time being, and they avoid us in return, which suits everyone just fine.

Satyrs

A lot of satyrs these days tend to stop thinking around groin level, but we remember the brightest members of this kith past, who could carry on a deep conversation *and* . . . well, you know. Some of them still carry on the tradition of being well rounded mentally as well as physically. You usually can't beat a grump satyr for philosophical debate. If you come across one of these more scholastically inclined Kithain, hold them close because they are some of the only ones who understand what it is we do. Firsthand knowledge of all those Greek oracles, I guess. Otherwise, satyrs are good for taking your mind off of your troubles for a night, as long as you don't mind being sore all over in the morning.

Sluagh

We have a great deal in common with these reclusive fae as well: They labor under a dark cloud like we do, and they know all too well the toll it extracts to keep secrets that no person was meant to know. Some of our most surprising aid during our return to this world has come from solitary sluagh who slid out of the shadows, offered us some measure of kindness or hospitality, then vanished back into the night before we could really thank them. It would be really interesting to compare notes sometime, that's for sure, if we could only get them to open up to us more.

Trolls

If any kith understands our dilemma and the place we once held in the hierarchy, it's the trolls. They share our sense of honor and sympathize with the conflicts of loyalty that we often face between revealing the visions we have had and the need to keep such troubling information from those who aren't prepared for it yet. Trolls also refuse to back down from a quest, no matter how terrible the odds may be, which we respect immensely. Many trolls once swore loyalty to our house, and though we lost contact during the Interregnum, as the Caul of Silence begins to fade we are starting to find more and more of them seeking our standard out once more. They are welcome in any of our lands, regardless.

Beyond the Gates: The Others

We've been back only briefly, and so we're still getting our bearings in the modern world; however, we've already encountered a few different forces out there that merit some attention.

Nunnehi

I don't know much about these mysterious kith, but from what I understand, some of them have ancient legends about a dark star appearing and the bloom of mysterious blue flowers that will accompany it, and that these were old tales centuries before our lord Jalendrel was even born. Supposedly these legends also talk of this event as foretelling some great disaster. I would dearly love to talk to one of the nunnehi and find out more about this legend; hopefully, someday I will.

Thallain

Like the Unseelie Houses and the Shadow Court, these dark fae are actually getting bold enough to come more into the light these days, and the other Kithain seem to do nothing about it. Are they that blind? These twisted mockeries of everything faerie are a sign of the impending return of the Fomorians, and yet the other Seelie do little other than give lip service to how they abhor their kind. Well, if the others can't or won't be bothered to do something about it, then we'll have to make up for the lack ourselves. Everything that's been said about mercy or justice goes out the window when dealing with the Thallain; these foul monsters are an abomination on the Kithain, and doing away with them is no worse than the modern-day use of antibiotics to kill a virus. Remember that if you meet one.

Centers of Power

Currently the house's main base of activity is New Orleans, where my brother and I are trying to organize and support the returning house members. Our other center of influence is the small hill town of Marvejols in southern France, traditional birthplace of our house and site of the recent discovery of the eponymously dubbed manuscript containing our history and some of our most sacred codes. Given our wandering natures, however, Beaumayn members can be found almost anywhere in the world by now—you just have to know how to look.

Members of Note

In any noble house, certain individuals stand forth. Whether the following members rise above the main body of our family or plumb the depths of villainy is for you to decide. As with any kin, the more we differ, the more it seems to mark how we are related.

Duke Jeremy Beaumayn and Count Brendan Beaumayn

My brother and I were two of the first of our house to remember ourselves, and I guess you'd call us the heads of House Beaumayn at the moment. We're fraternal twins—Remy's a minute and a half older, just so you know—and our Chrysalis came early, so we were brought into a freehold when we were still pretty young. We were both raised to think we were of House Eiluned, as do quite a few of our house before their true nature finally shines through. Remy was to be the head of the Principality of Jazz when he was old enough, and all was right with the world.

Then the revelations came. Lord Vandermere appeared, first innocently as our court magician, then showing his true colors by kidnapping Remy and trying to take over the court as part of some twisted scheme to locate the Iron Road. With the help of a commoner alliance and several Prodigal allies, however, I managed to thwart his designs and help bring Remy home. In the course of these struggles, I began getting visions as our true heritage gradually came to the surface, so when Remy returned, together we finally abandoned the colors of House Eiluned for the symbol of the dark star. We had to abandon control of the Principality of Jazz in the process, but with the arrival of more members of the house and the recovery of the Marvejols Script, we've definitely had our hands full. Things are improving, but so too is the Caul of Silence tearing, so now we're racing against time to try to brace ourselves for the day the rest of the fae remember who we truly are.

We were night and day growing up: Remy's a smokin' blues guitarist, handsome, cool and good with people; he dresses way better than I do, too, and is never seen without his trademark "blues guy" sunglasses. I, on the other hand, was the first sidhe to need glasses in decades, can never seem to get my hair to stay the way I like it and got hooked on computers early enough to give myself a nice pasty skin tone. He handles the speeches, diplomacy and other face-to-face PR work. I take care of letters, records, strategy, organization and other fun details like that. It's been a winning combination so far, so it seems.

Dame Lillian

This talented nocker wilder is responsible for perhaps the most important event since our return, the recovery of the Marvejols Script. An American who had only recently awakened to her faerie nature, Dame Lillian was an exchange student who was living in Marvejols for her time abroad when she came across a small cave in a hillside during a hiking trip. Making her way past the traps inside as only a nocker could, she discovered an ancient tome on an altar in the very last chamber.

Recognizing the surge of Glamour that marked it as a powerful Treasure, she brought it back to the States with her, where the magic of the text immediately called my brother and I up from New Orleans. Once we realized the enormity of her find, we knighted her on the spot and began deciphering the work in earnest. She has since shown a remarkable grasp of both ancient and modern French and proven herself a fierce fighter and able crafter as well. I would not hesitate to call her one of my closest friends.

Dame Lillian is a tall, pretty brunette with a friendly and unassuming manner that belies the sour reputation of her kith. Her temper is rare but white hot when kindled, as more than one foe has discovered to his regret. She especially loves working in theatrical set design and is currently awaiting her freshman year at a small college in the Kingdom of Apples.

Lord Vandermere

Every evil legend ever told about the Harbingers of Exodus finds expression in Lord Vandermere. Not much else is known about him or his past, though, save that he's ruthless, hellishly clever and utterly dedicated to the Exodus and the goals of Geremin's Heresy. He's a formidable threat by himself, having mastered a frightening array of Arts and gotten possession of a number of powerful Treasures as well. He usually makes little effort to hide his sinister designs and actually seems to enjoy flaunting his image as a "dark wizard"—black cloak, sinister props and all. Don't be fooled, though; he has more than enough power to back up his reputation.

What puzzles me is how this obviously Unseelie magician has taken the leadership of the Harbingers of Exodus, with its largely Seelie backing. Perhaps he presents a different face to them, or maybe his twisted goals really do conform with their narrow view of reality. Regardless of the real reason, Vandermere is supremely dangerous and must be stopped before he brings the wrath of all the Kithain down on us again.

Sir Thomas Magbane

Sir Magbane is perhaps the most puzzling of the members of our house to awaken to himself since our return. Born into a Gwydion household, this somber and solitary knight was one of the first to reclaim his heritage when I announced our return, and he was instrumental in defeating the plans of Lord Vandermere. Since then, however, it seems that despite our once close friendship, he believes I am destined to serve the Harbingers of Exodus and he has sworn to prevent that from happening. In human form, he's tall and imposing, with an athletic frame and confident gait. In fae form, his features sharpen, his cloak swirls about him restlessly and his eyes softly glow like an animal's. He is also a master swordsman, and his treasured long sword is never far from his grasp.

Since he broke away to begin his strange crusade, stories have begun to circulate about this mysterious wanderer: that he can change into a wildcat and stalk his foes undetected, that he has slain a half-dozen Dauntain single handedly, even that he has died and returned to life through strange magic. Whatever the truth of these rumors, I only hope my friend comes to his senses soon and realizes that our goals are one. Right now, though, he is a political wildcard in a house already too torn by politics.

Delphine Achidou

Delphine is a piskie and a native of Marvejols who became a friend of Dame Lillian during her stay there and who helped her recover the Script and keep it safe from the larcenous efforts of a gang of wilders under Vandermere's control. We offered her a title for her actions, but she simply laughed and said that she was happy knowing that she'd done her friend a favor. Now she's overseeing the founding of a freehold in a small café in town; she also acts as a guide for those of our house who wish to travel to France and reopen some of our old centers of power. All her mortal friends know is that Delphine will disappear for days or even a week at a time, but she always comes back with a few more stories to tell.

Like most of her kith, Delphine is small and thin with bright eyes and a perpetual bounce in her step. Her smile is contagious and her hands seldom stop moving. Those who would bully her on account of her size, however, are in for a rude surprise—her kicks have downed trolls more than twice her size. She has a passion for dancing and usually insists that her contacts meet her at a club near town. She gives extra respect to those who can keep up with her on the dance floor all night.

Treasures

Being held prisoner doesn't do much for your choice of accessories; nonetheless, we have found some of our old house Treasures and begun making new ones. Here are a few we have recovered so far.

Masquer's Eyes

Rare Treasure, Level 4

This Treasure is actually a pair of normal, if very exquisitely decorated, domino masks. When activated, they create a connection between the wearers, allowing the two to share senses and even emotions at range. The user dons the mask and spends 1 point of Glamour, and the other Kithain may see and hear everything her counterpart does as long as the mask is worn. She may even borrow her friend's voice, as long as her friend consents to the message. By expending 1 point of Glamour, the user may also use her friend's perceptions to cast cantrips that require a line-of-sight target. Such cantrips cost 1 extra point of Glamour beyond their usual expenditure to cast.

Additionally, if the two share any deep personal oathbonds—friendship, love, adoption, etc.—they may sense the other's *general* emotional and physical state by making a Perception + Empathy roll (difficulty 6). The Beaumayn brothers are the only known owners of such a Treasure at this time, but there are rumors of others at large.

Passion Bracelet

Rare Treasure, Level 1 to 3 (variable)

Dame Lillian specializes in crafting these Treasures. They appear as simple cloth or silver bracelets but in reality act as Glamour or Willpower "batteries," storing magic or resolve for their owners until it is needed. Given the great stresses we face, these bracelets are a godsend. Cloth bracelets are always woven with a changeling's favorite colors and hold Glamour, while silver ones are inscribed with the wearer's name and hold Willpower. Each can hold a number of the appropriate type of points up to the level of the Treasure. To add or remove points, one need only concentrate for a moment—this does not count as an action. So far only a few bracelets are known to exist, personal gifts from Dame Lillian all, but as her talent grows more will no doubt be forthcoming.

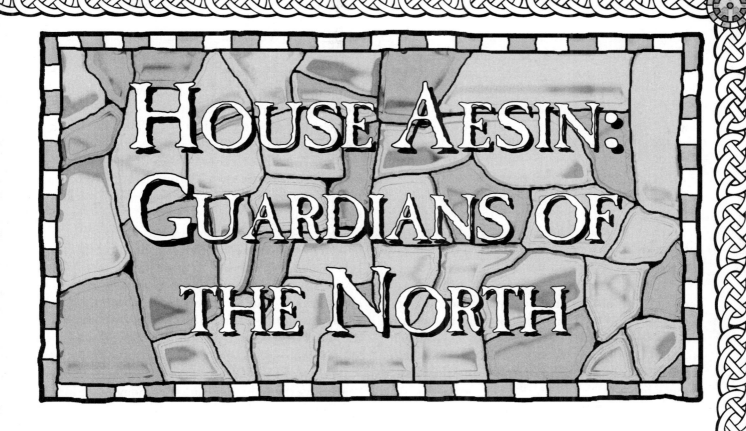

HOUSE AESIN: GUARDIANS OF THE NORTH

When I came ere long the war troop bold
were   watching   and   waking   all:
with burning brands and torches borne,
they showed me my sorrowful way.
    —Havesmál, Olive Bray translation

Vengeance Night

Ingirun's eyes were filled with madness as she plunged the dagger deep into her heart. She couldn't bear the sight of the dead bodies that surrounded her and her loyal forces. They were all family members. Her brother's war against her had forced her to take action. This was the outcome. The chilly night held the acrid, copper smell of fresh blood in the air. The odor traveled from nose to nose among those who stood within the fallen stone walls of the stronghold.

Rigall, Ingirun's brother, had murdered her children, and his corrupted thinking had led him to accuse her of betraying the war order. Of course, their parents had believed Rigall, the rightful leader of the order, and began to hunt down Ingirun's allies. The War of Courts had begun.

The war against the Jotunns suffered because of this. For eons the war order had protected all living beings against the Dark Dream and its creatures, but when the war began the order had to rely more and more on the support of outsiders. Fortunately for all fae, during the final nine battles, the Ancients kept a truce and once more stood on the same side. This resulted in the Jotunns' defeat and the Ancients' decision to leave for the Far Shores.

From that point Ingirun had to deal only with her brother. She had offered him a truce but he refused, so she gathered all her forces into one final strike against her brother's stronghold, and this was the result: the almost complete annihilation of the order's Seelie Court. Her mind couldn't bear it. Her heart ached. All her tears were not enough to water the graves of those who lay dead around her. Through blurred eyes, she counted fallen family members, innocent Aesin who had died because of her rivalry with her brother.

She felt no pain as she cut her heart out—a signal to her that it had already broken—and threw it high into the air, as if to satisfy the looming crimson star in the skyline that heralded the end of the war. She had seen it once long ago when the war against the Dark Dream began, and she understood that the Eye of Balor was here to mock her.

Joachim, Ingirun's lover, stared at the woman he loved as she cut out her heart and with the last ounce of her strength threw it high into the air. He could see the powerful trail of Glamour that followed her heart as it traveled upward, silhouetted against the red star that shone in the dark night. A great explosion filled the area with a light so bright that all present had to close their eyes not to be blinded. When the light vanished the star was gone as well, and he could see Ingirun falling toward the bloodstained ground beside her dead brother. He rushed forward just in time to catch her lifeless body in his arms.

"The Ancients are gone!" All turned to see who uttered the words. It was a sweet, young voice that lingered in the air. As they turned, the Aesins' eyes met with the Sisters Three—the Norns. They stood upon the balcony that extended from one of the towers. It didn't take long to realize that the words were Urd's, the young woman who attracted more men with her beauty than did the most beautiful sidhe.

Her sister Verdandi, a woman who could easily be mistaken for a mother with her matronly look, spoke next. "Past and present have collided."

From the shadows of the balcony's corner the old crone Skuld stepped forward. Her face could frighten the meanest Redcap if she wished it to. "The future awaits, young ones. Choose one now. Use wisdom in your choice. The paths of sorrow lie ahead. Make the journey a joyful one." No one spoke. No one dared to speak when the sisters were present. Minutes passed and the Norns said nothing.

Not a sound was in the air when the quietness was broken by the sweet sound of a female voice. "I choose. I claim my family's throne." Ragnelf, Ingirun and Rigall's younger sister, stepped forward. No one disputed her claim; no one wanted another succession war. They were all tired of warring amongst themselves. The actions that they had been forced to take tonight must never happen again. Seelie or Unseelie, they were all family.

The young wilder gracefully stepped onto the balcony above the large courtyard. For a moment she looked upon all those who lay dead beneath her, then she turned her attention to the survivors. "The war is over. What you see here is the result of the atrocities committed in an act of vengeance and despair. I, who knew of my brother's betrayal, stayed neutral throughout the war. Does this make me less guilty of the events transpiring? No, it makes me even guiltier. I watched as a great injustice was committed, not just to the followers of my sister, but also to those who did not know and were not able to act. My wounds are as large as yours. But they must heal. It will take time, but we will prevail. Our restoration begins now. As is my right, I hereby disband the Aesin war order. We must change with the times, and so we will lay the foundation for a new era. From now and to eternity we will be known as House Aesin, the northern guardians. We will act as one, be as one. We are family and we will never again war among ourselves. We shall dedicate ourselves to the true battle— against the Jotunns—and all who speak of us will call us living legends!"

Lexicon

Aesir/Vanes — Mortal name for Ancients

Alfheim — Arcadia

Ancients — Tuatha de Danaan

Bifrost — Bridge (trod) that connects Arcadia with Midgard

Heimdall — Bifrost's Guardian

Jotunns — Fomorians

Midgard — Earth

Ragnarök — End times that lead to the rebirth of the world

Volva — Wise one; woman versed in the Arts and acting as a spiritual leader

A Lesson in Aesin

Our names are many. Alfar, sidhe, dreamlords . . . but none of them matter. We are Aesin, proud guardians of the Dreaming. We exist because we never let the road of pain and sorrow weaken us. From the hard journey comes strength—the strength to never surrender to the darkness even at the cost of our lives.

I am Beatrice ap Aesin, Volva and amateur Skald. Your mothers have allowed me to continue your training so you may join the sisterhood of Volvas one day. This is a great responsibility but also a great joy. I trust you to never reveal anything you hear to any outsiders.

Let us begin.

The Mythic Age

Just as other Kithain, we see the Mythic Age as a joyful age, but unlike them we also look back upon it with sadness and contempt. Yes, the mortals had not yet rebelled, but the fact is that Vengeance Night took place during this age. For us this age was one of blood, war and injustice.

Glamour flowed freely across the realms, but unlike others we refused to immerse ourselves in too much power and waste Glamour without cause—we were not corrupted. Maybe that is why we fared better during the later years?

The Sundering

With the passing of one age comes a new. We entered a time of hatred and disbelief not long after mortals found iron. They hunted us for eternal power and wisdom, but for a time we fought back, and unlike in other parts of the world, we managed to calm them. Secretly we withdrew, leaving only memories of us, as the newly created Escheat bid us.

These memories, although twisted by mortal minds, came to the surface when mortals began to worship the Ancients, now known as the Aesir. Once more, we moved among the mortals as we did during the Mythic Age—as gods. Glamour flowed to us again but ended when the war against the spreading faith called Christianity began.

We gave some of our knowledge freely to the mortals who worshipped us. Soon thereafter Vikings began to rage across the world. I see you understand the reason why one of the first Viking attacks recorded was against a Christian church. It is true. We were behind the attack. Nevertheless, the Vikings soon created their own agendas as well. Many of them founded new kingdoms and created what they saw as a vast empire. But in the shadows we governed their actions.

Together with our subjects, Aesin warriors fought bravely. In the end, however, we lost when the citizens of our kingdoms converted to the other side.

The Shattering

For the first time since we came into existence, we lost a war. Although our kingdoms converted to Christianity, there were some mortals who still believed in us, so some of our house stayed to protect them while others fled to the Summer Lands, or Alfheim. What happened with the emigrants to the Summer Lands is unknown to us, a mystery that waits for an answer. We stayed here in Midgard for as long as possible, but when the High King declared the withdrawal to Alfheim, we obeyed without question.

Gods

In **Changeling: The Dreaming**, a game of dreams, legends and mysteries, most truths are like two-edged swords. In this world the treatment of Gods is delicate not to be taken lightly. Thus the discovery of one's true origin can be the basic foundation to a chronicle.

From the Tales of Maria Magdalena Sofia Aesin

Long ago, during the time of the Mythic Age, our parents still walked amongst the fae of this realm. Now, whereas the Celtic culture knew of the old ones as the Tuatha de Danaan, the mortals of the far north knew of them as Vanes.

With the passing of time, the Vanes court met with another gathering of Gods, the Aesir. Where the Vanes were peaceful, the Aesir were a court intent on waging war. In this case the war was directed mostly at the evil Jotunns, known as Fomorians in Celtic lands.

The biggest difference between the two was that the Vanes had the ability to utilize magic, but the other court lacked that ability. The Aesir looked upon their sister court with envy and, while never trying to take the knowledge from them, they desired it more then anything. For a long time the two courts kept peace between them, but when the Aesir killed one of the Vanes because of her witchcraft, a war broke out between them. It was a bloody one, only coming to an end when it was decided that the two courts would join and become one. From this joining sprang the War order Aesin. At least that is what the story tells us.

The Interregnum

Because of the Mists we know little of this era. Nevertheless, I will share what my memories allow me. In the dark mountains of Alfheim lay Castle Aesin clothed in ice and snow. At the feet of the mountains there was a vast forest. This was our domain, our kingdom. From there we ruled our subjects and trained while we waited for the day when there would once more be a need for our services. Beneath the full moon we danced among the trees, enacting countless rituals that would strengthen us. I have vague memories of a war, where a young Ailil led an uprising and forced us to besiege them in a cavern. Needless to say, we defeated them. I think, though I am not sure, that we used the repercussions of the war as an excuse for exiling the other houses. They would be our eyes and ears in Midgard. Unfortunately, this tactic failed as they became both blind and deaf to what was happening in Alfheim.

Second Resurgence

Just like in the elders' stories and prophecies, a crimson star appeared on the skyline. We dispatched a patrol of hunters and warriors to the Forest of Lies, but they never returned. I remember a battle not far from the borders of Alfheim. I see myself kneeling by the side of a dead man and casting my most powerful cantrips against creatures of darkness. Then my memories go blank. The last thing I remember is traveling over Bifrost to Midgard, listening to the sad tones of Heimdall's horn. There is no question about it. The Jotunns are coming for us and we must do whatever it takes to stop them.

Our Missing Queen

Disaster struck as we walked the silver path. Without warning, foul creatures, most likely the Fell, attacked us and chaos erupted. During the battle, our dear Queen Ragnelf vanished without a trace. Our questions about her fate remain unanswered. Some have left on a quest to search for her, and if they succeed, they will receive a large compensation. We need Ragnelf's guidance in quenching the darkness. Until she returns, High Lord Magnhildr rules House Aesin.

Shattered Dreams

Our plan was to return to our ancient homelands and make our stand there. These dreams were shattered when the Dreaming placed most of us here in Concordia. Speculations arose that since we found these lands during the Sundering it was our duty to now protect them. None of us knows the truth, but the Dreaming must have placed us here so that we would restore fae society. Madness has spread throughout commoner society, and commoners now believe that they can sit on our thrones and rule what is rightfully ours. This must end. We all have our place to fill in fate's grand design, and the commoners must learn their true place. If not, we will lose and the Jotunns will rule after Ragnarök.

Aesin Life

He who fights with monsters might take care lest he thereby become a monster. And if you gaze for long into an abyss, the abyss gazes also into you.

—Friedrich Wilhelm Nietzsche

Our lives are not easy. Each new day brings with it new trials to overcome. Since the dawn of the Dreaming, although we try to live "normal" lives, we of Aesin blood have acted as guardians against the Jotunn Dream. Most of us prefer to live in natural surroundings since it reminds us of our ancient home. Still, there are those who have begun to adapt to the city lifestyle as well.

In the new life we now live, we still carry on our old traditions. The women rule the home, while the men perform the hunt and war. We share different responsibilities and by doing so we become more than a house—we become a family.

The Curse

I can see that you despise your mortal flesh. For us it must be a curse from the Dreaming to repay us for the atrocities committed on Vengeance Night. But why has it struck all the others? It is true that it protects us from Banality. However, why must the Dreaming be so cruel to us? The eternal beauty and godly appearance we had in Alfheim is lost, and many fear that our new host bodies will pollute our minds and cause us to go insane. Rumor has it that it has happened once already.

True Faith

During their return, no Aesin sidhe took the body of a Christian mortal. Ever since the war against the Christian religion during the Viking Age, members of the house find the faith repelling. If faced with Christian True Faith, the character must roll her Willpower, difficulty 6, or immediately withdraw from the scene.

The truth is that our minds are as strong as ever, but mortal flesh limits us. In order to stay sane most of us, including myself, see mortal bodies as mere clothing. We now have the opportunity to study their society, and this is something we have to do right now if we are to ever subdue them. In time, they will kneel to our superiority.

Vengeance Night (April 30)

Even today, House Aesin remembers the terrible night that came to pass several millennia ago. On April 30, the house repays the Dreaming for what we once took. We light a large bonfire and, under the supervision of the house ruler, one Unseelie Aesin from each occupation (Volva, mother, warrior, hunter, berserker and skald), each dressed in red, walks into the fire. Some would call this "paying tithe to hell," but House Aesin sees it as a repayment for the crimes our lust for revenge caused. It is a great honor to be chosen as one of the sacrifices, for we accept only the finest. We know that such great courage is rewarded by an immediate return to Alfheim, where the honorees oversee the preparations for our coming war against the Jotunns. We also believe that the ritual heralds the coming of spring and summer.

The Virtue Council

With the founding of House Aesin, our lives changed. Following the path of destiny, Queen Ragnelf created the Virtue Council. Nine Aesin sit in the council with a majority of Unseelie, as the court with most members has more seats on the council. Currently there are six Unseelie and three Seelie that occupy the seats. Their purpose is to decide on matters of grave importance for the house and to act as judges during special trials.

Connection to Nature

Every flower, mineral, animal and beast has a beautiful soul. Unfortunately some, as is the case with Jotunns, do not understand what it means to have one. We of House Aesin are convinced that the Dreaming's true magic lies within ourselves. When we can connect with the inner essence of our souls, we become equally powerful to those who came before. Nature is the perfect place for this process. It is purifying for our minds and heart, and we feel safe among our most loyal subjects, the animals.

Men and Women

Our men dress in furs and robust clothing so that they can go into battle with ease. We women dress in elaborate clothing, usually with runes embroiled along the arms. In our culture jewelry and weapons measure our status. Our jewels are made of amethyst, silver, gold and bronze. Mothers tend to have the most jewelry.

Women

In our society, each woman plays a large role in day-to-day business. Men revere us as honorable life givers, matriarchs, and wise knowledge keepers. Most of us tend to spend our lives studying the transcendent powers of the Dreaming, while others such as myself become Volvas.

We are the caretakers of the old, the children and the dying. Never wavering, we go where there is a need for us. Women raise all Aesin childlings, teaching them discipline, responsibility and living by the virtues.

All these things we do, and still we find time to fight Jotunns and govern others. The burden is heavy, but we endure. Look at Urd, Verdandi and Skuld, the Norns, three women in whose hands the fate of us all lies. If that is not a proof of women's capabilities, you will never find any.

Volvas

Those of us who desire to become Volvas, like you, must know that we—sisters—have an even larger responsibility toward the faerie community than others have. We are those whom men call upon before going into battle, the ones whom everyday Aesin fear and

revere. We are women with powers beyond regular fae, proficient in cantrips and soothsaying. A Volva is proud of her heritage and carries on the traditions of House Aesin without doubting the ways of our house. The wooden staff we gain at our inauguration into the Volva sisterhood is something we proudly carry with us wherever we go.

Mothers

Mothers are those who raise our childlings. All of you have one or more mothers. They have accepted the joy of introducing newborn Aesin to our way of living. When childlings reach the age where they will pass the Fior-Righ, as you soon will, the mother hands over the responsibility to a master. In this case, they chose me to prepare you for the coming trial.

Do not worry, childlings, the mothers you had will always be with you and watch over you. All of you hold a special place in their heart. Most of the older Aesin turn to their mothers for help or advice, even when they are several millennia old. Even I still turn to my dear mother for help at times when I am unable to come up with an answer to a problem.

Skalds

Our female skalds are a minority. I am one of the lucky few that our house allows to use the epithet *amateur skald*. Women who become skalds focus their entertaining ability on singing and poetry. I have found my calling in turning prophecies into poems.

Norns

Feared, loved, all knowing—these words describe the common opinion concerning the Sisters Three, rulers of the Adhene called Moirae. Since the dawn of the Dreaming these women have spun their threads of fate for all living creatures.

Scholars of our house believe that the Norns are the true source of Aesin blood, and the sisters have never done anything to dispute this claim. They are independent of House Aesin, and we have no control over them, yet the sisters come to us from time to time with their cryptic prophecies and warnings.

Men

Our Aesin men have large muscles, gleaming eyes and long gold-brown hair that falls down their back and upper torso. Just thinking about them makes my knees weak. When you become older you will understand.

The men take everything they do even more seriously than we women do. Their responsibility is not only to fight the Dark Dream, but also to provide their family with what we need. I have yet to hear a complaint about something done by an Aesin man; they make sure to succeed at all cost. Regrettably, they are equally good at bragging.

Take everything they tell you with a pinch of salt. Impressing you is what they want. Men love to talk about their kills, women and weapons. In the male society, their weapons measure their status. We women could care less about their blades and axes, but by pretending we do, we give them hope and confidence.

Hunters

Our hunters are our greatest weapon in the war against the Jotunns. Their ability to track is unmatched by any other house, and in this age we have a great need for them in order to find our lost kinain and house members. The hunters are now tracking them down, and with each group, a Volva follows to make contact with possible new allies.

Warriors

These are honorable men who spend their lives studying the art of war. Without them, we would have lost our eternal war a long time ago. Unlike skalds, the warriors and hunters go through extensive physical training, and sometimes we even send them out on life-threatening missions to see whether they are worthy of becoming Aesin warriors. Their entire education is like a second Fior-Righ.

Berserkers

Berserkers are the cursed elite force among the warriors. These thirteen men accept the heavy burden of protecting our house ruler by donning ancient, magical armor that shields them from all attacks with weapons and allows them to fight beyond their regular capacity. The problem is that once unleashed, berserkers are impossible to stop until they are dead or we have won. Wearing the berserker armor poisons the mind, and their sanity is the price they pay for becoming a member of this respected and feared group.

Skalds

Legends, songs, stories and music would become forever lost if it were not for the skalds. Those who choose this profession gain their training from an older skald who wants them to take his place when he is gone. Fame comes to you if you manage to get a skald to come to your home during feast times. Skalds help keep us dedicated to our aims by telling ancient tales and inspiring us in battle.

Cross-gender Occupations

The professions given above are the traditional divisions by sex within our house. Naturally, there are some who prefer to step outside the bounds of tradition and follow a path usually taken by the opposite sex. As a woman granted skald status, I am one of these. There are women who become feared and respected warriors. Though not encouraged, neither are such cross-sex attempts actively dissuaded. So long as the individual can stand teasing and prove him- or herself, acceptance eventually comes.

Fior-Righ

We value our connection to nature, and this is why we allow it to become an important part of our Fior-Righ. Unlike most other houses, our test of survival is for *real*. If you are not worthy enough to become a wilder, you will die. We cannot afford any weakness in the war, because success will be impossible unless we are strong and efficient. Soon it will be your time for testing. I can already see your eyes burning with the lust of an Aesin, but calm down. If you wish to live, you must listen carefully during your training.

As a young childling, perhaps age nine or ten, you'll wake up—boys and girls together, as a family—somewhere in a forest. You'll have no tools or weapons to use except your mind and no one to rely on except your fellow Aesin. Danger will lurk behind every tree and bush, and you must function as a family to survive.

If you survive for a week, we dispatch a band of hunters that tracks you down and brings you back to us. When you return, the High Lord performs the Saining ceremony, where you'll learn your true name. Then it is time to take the oath of virtues to become a true Aesin Wilder.

Children, even if one of you fails and dies, you should not feel ashamed. You have served your house in honor and you accept death before the dishonor of returning home weakened and dismayed. I assure you that as long as you live by the virtues, you will manage to survive. There are those whom we thought would die, but to our surprise they came home sooner then we imagined.

The Owl and the Runes: Our Blazon

Our blazon carries with it both history and power. In past times it is said we owned the ability to shape-shift to the form of an owl. It is a wise bird but also a strong predator. You can see this symbolism on our beautiful blazon: A golden owl stands centered against a grey background. On either side lie golden runes, Uruz and Ansuz, which represent our primal powers and strengths.

House Boon and Ban

Nature's Touch: More than most other changelings, members of House Aesin have a strong connection to nature. As lords of man and animal alike, Aesin changelings have the ability to speak with forest animals (e.g., elk, squirrel, bear, deer, owls, etc.). Make an Intelligence + Empathy roll against your Banality +3 each time your character wishes to understand an animal. You may speak for the number of minutes equal to your successes.

Empathic Blindness: While still caring for their subjects, changelings belonging to House Aesin have a tendency to have a master–slave relationship with them. Nevertheless, they feel obligated to protect their loyal servants, and occasionally they might feel something else for them. In the end, however, Aesin keep their Deep Dreaming flaw, although the Mists upon reentry in Midgard have weakened it. They receive a +3 difficulty on all Social rolls involving anyone other than nobles. There is only one other exception. For some reason the Dreaming neglects this curse when dealing with the family that belongs to the mortal body who hosts the newly arrived sidhe.

The Oath of Virtues

My eternal soul now lies with House Aesin.
I swear by the forests and mountains of my home that
I will uphold the traditions and customs of House Aesin.
Knowing I reach safety, I seek shelter beneath the wings of the owl.
If my oath is broken, may the Dreaming strip me of all privileges and never let me forget who I was and what I have become.

When the wilder swears this oath, others considers her to be an adult Aesin with all house privileges. The Aesin gains 2 dots to allocate among the abilities she has for her occupation. If the oath is broken, she loses *all* points in the abilities where the 2 dots were placed. To symbolize belonging to House Aesin, the wilder receives a shield bearing the blazon of the house.

Treasures

These Treasures represent our history. Garbled descriptions of them have passed down in the knowledge of mortals and spawned many tales concerning their making, their wielders and their powers. Thus, our Treasures have served to fire the imaginations of Dreamers from early times to the present.

Eilaf (Unique Treasure, Level 4)

This long bow once belonged to the Ivalde, a great warrior who died during the ninth and final battle against the Jotunns. The Volvas guard this bow until the day when a new warrior whose skills match Ivalde's comes to them. An arrow fired from this bow never misses its target and inflicts aggravated damage. The bow rests within a crystal casing in Caer Aesin, deep in the dark forests of Norrland, Sweden.

Tapestry of Fate (Legendary)

Whether it truly exists or not is unknown to the fae. According to stories, the tapestry contains every true name that there is, as well as the fate of the Dreaming. The power and knowledge it holds are invaluable. Lost long ago, it is rumored to be everywhere from a sluagh houshold to under the Silvered Sea. Many have left in search of it, but none have returned. One thing is for certain: The finder will probably draw the wrath of the Norns upon him.

Berserker Armor (Uncommon Treasure, Level 3)

This ornate armor shields those who wear it from all attacks with weapons and allows them to fight beyond their regular capacity (bestowing 5 extra levels of OK to their health). The greatest house secret is that the armor is vulnerable to magical attacks or attacks made with the bare hand. Though powerful, the armor exacts a price: Once those wearing berserker armor are unleashed, they are impossible to stop until they are dead or their side has won the battle. Further, wearing the armor poisons the mind, and the warriors who do so become insane over time. Each time the armor is worn, the wearer must make a Wits roll (difficulty 7). If he fails to achieve any successes, he loses a point of Wits and moves one step along the road to Bedlam. When Wits drop to 1, the warrior becomes permanently insane and disappears into the Dreaming. Only one such victim has ever been retrieved and restored to his right mind, and he never again picked up a sword.

Politics

We rarely use threats or manipulation to achieve our own agendas. Our way is the direct approach. Why spend time lying when we can get what we want by telling the truth? Our words are as binding as an oath, and this honesty is what makes us trustworthy.

Understand that others must feel that they can trust us on our words. *If* you decide to rely on the frailty of manipulation, plotting revenge is something best done in the dark, where no one can know or act against you. Make sure that you do not act against House Aesin's interests and that few, if any, of our house discover your tactics. You will not be well thought of or trusted for using such wiles.

The Nine Virtues

Only once have we strayed from this path, and it ended with the War of Courts. This must never happen again, and therefore the nine virtues have gone from guidance to laws. Live by them, honor them and cherish their wisdom. They supercede any law or practice laid down by either the Seelie or Unseelie Courts.

Courage

Always stand for what you believe in, even if you are alone. Injustice must never go unpunished or unopposed. Do whatever you deem necessary, but do not remain silent.

Truth

Never do or say anything that causes you to be dishonest. If you act dishonestly or lie for some reason, prepare to take the consequences.

Honor

Honor is different for all of us, but it is akin to an emotion. It is knowing that you did the right, decent thing and that you treat your subjects in a fashion they deserve. Be humble, but never let others take anything for granted.

Fidelity

Once honorably oath sworn, you must never break that bond. Remain loyal to your master, but also see to it that your subjects are loyal to you. If they are not, you must break the bond, as they are unworthy of it. You will pay the penalty for this, but better that than tied by oath to those who are unworthy or who are monsters.

Discipline

Discipline is a pattern of thinking and acting that defines who you are. Though we constantly strive for discipline, it is hard to master, for there are many different kinds. Warriors might have physical discipline, while scholars seek intellectual mastery. Never scoff at another's chosen form of discipline merely because it differs from your own.

Hospitality

We are one family and should help each other whenever we can. Treat others with kindness and respect. After all, there might come a time when you need hospitality yourself. We grant those who ask it formal hospitality of three days and 10 miles. During that time we extend food, shelter, the right of entertainment and our promise of nonaggression, even to our most dire enemies. We expect them to comport themselves honorably in return. At the end of that time, those we have hosted are required to leave (unless it is impossible due to weather, illness or immediate danger) and travel at least 10 miles away from our holding. Failure to do so may result in grave punishment or even a battle to the death.

Industry

You must work long and hard if you wish to rise in rank. You must *earn* your title; we won't give it to you simply because of your birth. Our leaders are those who work hardest and accomplish the most. We of House Aesin always get the job done—one way or another.

Self-Reliance

Do what you can for yourself. Only when a task involves things you are incapable of doing should you ask for help. Do what you can for others, but teach them to rely more on themselves than on you.

Perseverance

If at first you do not succeed, try things another way. Never do anything that is not worth your time and effort. Doing such things only gains you credit for being stupid. Each of us has at least one special talent. Use it, perfect it!

The Court Tenets

We do not ignore the tenets of the Winter and Summer Courts; we simply modify them according to our Nine Virtues.

Winter Codex

Change Is Good.

Change can be both terrifying and joyful, as we have learned from history. It is a natural force that must never cease lest things become stagnant. Reverting back to old ways is not necessarily wrong. It is still a change.

Glamour Is Free.

There will always be a supply of Glamour to find. It does not matter if it is the seductive dark or pure, warm Glamour. This substance is what sustains us, and to refuse it is to deny yourself.

Honor Is a Lie.

Claiming honor without believing in it is disgraceful. Honor is not court or kith bound, and unless it is looked upon with respect and honesty, it becomes nothing more than a lie.

Passion before Duty

There is little to say on this part of the codex. Our duty *is* our passion.

Summer Aesin

During the War of Courts, countless Seelie fell beneath our court's blades. We were not the only ones who suffered during this tragic event. These days we find comfort in knowing that the Norns decided their fate long ago. We merely followed our path when undoing them.

Put your feelings about Rigall and his actions aside and understand that our Seelie are not necessarily evil. Just like us, they uphold the customs of House Aesin.

What we differ in is our views on life. Improbable as it may seem, there are occasions when we are in agreement. We are, after all, one family. Ideologies aside, you must never forget that all of us bear the marks of both courts. Denying our dual nature is foolish, and this is our reason for embracing both summer and winter.

Summer Codex

Death before Dishonor

Dying in the name of House Aesin is honorable. Living as a coward is not.

Love Conquers All.

Yes, but the Seelie have tried to define love into one single concept. Love is Unseelie. It is a force of change and is different to all of us.

Beauty Is Life.

Ask yourself what beauty is for you, then answer this: Would I give up my life to protect what I find most beautiful?

Never Forget a Debt.

Forgetfulness can be catastrophic. If you do not remember your debts, you might end up in a situation where you have no allies, for you have dishonored friends by failing to repay them what you owe. Only the foolish or dishonorable choose this path.

The Escheat

Right of Demesne

Until now this law has been unnecessary. All of the Dreaming's children knew their rightful place, but with the commoner rebellion we have to implement this part of the Escheat officially.

Right to Dream

House Aesin forbids you to waste precious Glamour on feeble creatures such as mortals. They are supposed to supply *us* with Glamour, not the other way around. If a mortal cannot produce the nourishment that you need, he is expendable, but you must protect those who can.

Right of Ignorance

For many centuries, we have kept this law for the good of our people. With the return of the Jotunns, we are no longer sure that we can afford to. It is imperative that mortals know whom to serve in the coming war.

Right of Rescue

Save a life, earn a boon.

Right of Safe Haven

Freeholds are sacred—on this we agree. Right now we can afford to keep the war outside freeholds, but that may change soon.

Right of Life

Even the Dreaming must understand how foolish this law is. We are fighting an eternal war here, and there will be death on both sides. Killing outside of war is anathema, and punishment must come to perpetrators. You would do well to remember that we only implement this law when it comes to faerie life.

The Shadow Court

A chaotic world is exactly what the fools of the Shadow Court wish to create. Although we embrace Winter, we are nowhere near these maniacs. Changelings who belong to the Court of Shadows want the winter to be eternal, never allowing summer to come. They deny our existence as creatures of change. The Dreaming thrives on change, and if it disappears, we will all die and the Jotunn Dream will rule the Autumn World. The Shadow Court is a threat that we must remove.

Relations

Exiled houses, mad commoners—what kind of world have we returned to? None of them sees the coming danger. As soon as the Jotunns' conquest of the Dreaming is final, they will come here. Our decisions, our guidance are what stand in the way of eternal slavery and despair. The time has come to end that which has been and allow a new world to take form. If we wish to avoid the dark future that threatens us we must cooperate and make sure to once more function as one. For us to accomplish this, we need allies and friends, but our path is not easy. Enemies lurk around the corner even among those we consider trustworthy.

Noble Relations

House Ailil

Fae more skilled in manipulation are hard to find. It is as if they have it in their blood to dupe others and always come out on top. Though disgusting to us, this house has much influence among the other Unseelie. They are, according to rumor, the leaders of the Shadow Court, and we must somehow destroy their mad plan. Never trust them, and keep them close so you can watch the children of the canny dragon. If you let them fool you, they will use you and those you care for in ways you wouldn't dare to dream of. It may be that Ailil must be destroyed, but if we could cure them of their manipulative ways, they could be a force of great use against the true enemy.

House Balor

House Balor is an adversary on all levels. These children of the Jotunns have managed to fool the other Kithain by claiming relationship with us. The truth is that they stole the blood from captive sidhe during the War of Trees, and when they saw that their defeat came closer, they merged to form this house.

We want nothing to do with them. We see through the serpents' lies and wait for them to show their true colors to the others. When they have done that, we will strike back with vengeance for all the misery they have caused. If both you and the Dreaming forgive me, I must say that Vengeance Night will look like child's play in comparison.

House Beaumayn

Of all the Seelie houses, we have had the most conflicts with Baumayn. Once true nobles, they embraced the chill of iron and joined the crusades. Unlike Liam, which refused to accept punishment for its crimes, House Beaumayn served time in Alfheim's dark prisons. As they are allies to our friends in House Varich, we must try to accept Beaumayn members and forgive them for their actions. But as things stand right now, we barely tolerate them.

House Daireann

This is a house made up of warriors with great integrity. Unfortunately, not only their integrity is large—their mouths are about the same size. They cannot be trusted with secrets, but otherwise they are great friends and precious lovers. They come from Hibernia and other Celtic lands, and seeing them in action fills our hearts with hope. The Jotunns had better prepare for heavy causalities. Did you mention poison? No, they don't deal with such things! If you are so certain, you could ask them. With their penchant for blurting out everything they know, I'm sure they'd tell you.

House Dougal

This honorable house consists of flawed sidhe. They are the true creators of the Dreaming and take as much pride as we in what they do. Creations of House Dougal are among the most beautiful things you can ever imagine. We will not survive the Dream War unless we can convince them to supply us with what we need. This would not be a hard task if it were not for the fact that they are the puppets of House Gwydion. Where the falcon flies, the Dougals go. Break the link. Make them our allies.

House Eiluned

This is a house too important to ignore. Nobles of Eiluned have access to forgotten lore and hidden secrets that we need at a time like this. Such an alliance will not be cheap, but we must succeed. Find something valuable to them and trade with them, but never let them close to you. Never reveal any important secret to them, unless you wish others to know. As they sell secrets and knowledge to you, they do the same for others.

House Fiona

If they were as fierce in battle as they are in love, the Dark Ones would truly have a problem handling members of Fiona. If you ever fall in love with one of them, prepare to have your heart broken. The Fiona sidhe have a talent for falling in love and then going from one person to the next. On many occasions, they even go to mortals or commoners. Prejudice aside, they are in truth very stubborn and not easily frightened by danger, and for that they have my respect. Let them know of the danger that lies ahead and see to it that they understand what will happen with those they love if we lose.

House Gwydion

Summer lords is the name commonly used for these fae. Their strength and integrity make them worthy allies, and we could surely use them if they could put aside their prejudice against Unseelie fae. Some say that they once worked for the old Ancient Tyr, who, according to stories, was a true follower of Justice, but I must doubt that. Ancients never feared change, and this is something House Gwydion fears to excess. Their manipulative skills can almost stand in comparison with those of House Ailil. When dealing with them you are advised to trust your instincts rather than their words.

House Leanhaun

Think of Leanhaun and allow yourself to weep. These brave souls work hard for our continued survival. They spend their time musing creative mortals so that the worlds can heal. House Leanhaun dreams of a better world where there is no need for musing and where we all can walk as gods once more. If there is anything you can help these noble souls with—do it. They are truly worthy of our assistance.

House Liam

A Liam who dares to set a foot in our holdings without first begging formal hospitality will regret it the second he enters. House Aesin has nothing but contempt for these traitors. Their cooperation with the commoners in the Accordance War did not come as a surprise to us; they have nothing more to lose. It is a shame, however, that they show no signs of remorse; if they would do that, we could forgive them for their crimes. After all, we are *true* nobles, and being magnanimous comes with the territory.

House Scathach

There are no other "commoner nobles" in our eyes. Once we treated them poorly, but when they decided to remain and protect the subjects still in Midgard, this left our eyes clouded with tears and our hearts broken. Their nobility amazed us, and Ragnelf pronounced House Scathach to be nobles. It is an honor to make a friend in this house.

We have had plenty of disputes with the Scathach sidhe who returned to Alfheim with us. In honesty, we see *those* Scathach as nothing more then repulsive half sidhe–half mortals, not like their kin who remained in the Autumn World. Nevertheless, they are members of a house declared noble and must be treated as such.

House Varich

These nobles are proud allies of House Aesin and the sovereign rulers of the Inanimae. During our time in Alfheim, we worked closely together, and it is our hope that we can do so now as well. This gathering of nobles consists of strong and valiant warriors who work for change but, just as we do, wish to be in control of the changes. The only dispute we have with them is that they withdrew into Alfheim so early during the Shattering. This move makes us believe that they care more for their own safety than for those whom we must protect.

Gallain and Others

We have complex relationships with and thoughts concerning those not of the Great Houses. Some we find totally alien to our customs, while others who are called *alien* or *Gallain* we think of as being as common as boggans.

Adhene

Once the servants of the Dark Dream, these fae fell with their masters during the final battle in the Dreaming. As punishment, the Ancients imprisoned them and banned them from all silver paths. Recent activities in Midgard caused their release, and now we fear that they do the Jotunns' biddings here. The Norns have assured us that some of them wish to join us in our war against darkness to redeem past crimes. We must find those who are willing to switch sides and let them prove their trustworthiness to us. The rest of them who fight on the dark side are fair targets. We will find them and stop them by whatever means necessary.

Ancients

Once we respected them, but when they did not stop Rigall and chose his side, they became our adversaries. They were the reason that the events that ended with Vengeance Night unfolded, and we will never forgive them for that, even if it was the Norns' will.

Unfortunately, thanks to the prophecy we know that our destinies have a link with those of the Ancients. Unless they return, Ragnarök will never take place, and

this will cause the world to remain stagnant. Find them and shepherd them back to Midgard—by luring them to war if necessary. This time they do not have Rigall's forces to help them. Only when they arrive will the *final* battle begin.

Commoners

They are not to blame for losing their way. The fault lies with the five houses exiled earlier. If they had not allowed the formation of the now dissolved (thankfully) Parliament of Dreams, the commoners would still know their true place in society.

Although we need them in the war against the Jotunns, we cannot allow their crimes against our superiority to go unpunished. Find the leaders of their resistance groups and eliminate them. Show them that there is no room for disobedient commoners in this world.

When we have brought peace about and made them aware of the Dark Dream, they will thank us for coming back. Until then, commoners will hate and scorn us as oppressors. That consequence comes with being saviors of those who are ignorant of the need for salvation.

Gallain

None of us is sure on why these fae are called *Gallain* rather than accorded the same status as any other commoner. They are as much commoners as the satyrs or pooka, and we rule them accordingly. We value the freedom of spirit that fuels the clurichaun, the wisdom and connection with the Dreaming that the ghille-dhu have. We can spend hours staring at the selkies' alien beauty and listening to their songs and tales of the sea. But we do not think they should rule any more than the other commoners do.

Inanimae

Although we feel close to them and highly respect them, we acknowledge that Inanimae are under House Varich's jurisdiction. Unless an Inanimae has committed a crime, we leave them for the Varich fae.

Jotunns

Twisted, cunning creatures born of the worst dreams conceivable, Jotunns are so cruel that we cannot comprehend what goes on inside their minds. Their recent regroupings in the Dreaming made us return to Midgard. Rumors of direct encounters with them in battle have recently come to us but are still unconfirmed. We have dispatched messengers to investigate this matter.

It is our wish to wipe them out, but we cannot do that if we want a new mythic age to arise. According to the old prophecy, they will fight the Ancients during Ragnarök. Therefore, we must try to keep them at bay and push them back as much as we can while we try to get the Ancients to return to us.

Nunnehi

They are the original inhabitants of Concordia. Unfortunately, we have yet to meet one. Maybe we can become allies?

Prodigals

Other Kithain name most of the following creatures among the prodigals, or those who fell or turned away from us to become something other than fae. We have our own thoughts on each of these but also include some, such as animals, that most other fae ignore.

Animals

Just like mortals, animals constantly evolve, making them equally in need of our guidance. Imagine standing proud alongside the great and powerful bear as the two of you battle the Dark Dream, or think of the little squirrel that sneaks into enemy camps and spies on your behalf. Love them and become one with the animals' surroundings. Unfortunately, mortals fail to realize the greatness of nature and continue to destroy it. Just do what you can to ease the animals' pain. Maybe one day we can harvest dreams from animals as well. It is worth trying as a last resort.

Ghosts

Never deal with the dead unless you have someone who has experience with them accompanying you. Listen to them only if they are honored ancestors.

Mortals

Mortals are both our subjects and foes. History has taught us that they cannot be trusted; they will only turn on us. They need strict guidance from us, and that is what we will give them when the time is right. In the meantime, we use them as cattle, harvesting their dreams as we can. This is their true purpose for living. As you know, there might still be some kinain out there. Our hunters are doing their best to find them and bring them back into the fold.

There are those among them who make the commoners tremble with fear. These mortals, known as *Dauntains* and *Autumn People*, oppose us. We need to put an end to their rebellion, but caution is wise when dealing with them. More than one faerie has fallen beneath their Banality-infested touches.

Vampires

We have little knowledge of these creatures. When our paths crossed in ancient days, we met with some of them living in our forests. We closed a nonaggression pact with them. Unfortunately, when the Shattering came they saw a chance to break the agreement. I wonder whether they are still around. We have a score to settle with them.

Werewolves

For a murder committed, the Ancients forced one of their own to watch as his two sons fought each other until one was dead. The winning son, transformed into a wolf, escaped and spawned his own kin before the other Ancients caught up with him and chained him. His kin remain today. Once they were our allies, but because of an ancient mistake, we are now enemies. The Fenrir, as we call them, are a powerful gathering of warriors. Unlike our other allies, the Fianna, these shape changers value our Norse traditions.

Wizards

We of House Aesin have had little dealings with these powerful mortals. They are an intriguing threat, and that is why we lure them into dark forests and perform experiments on them.

Honored Individuals

All houses have at least a few notables whom most members look up to. House Aesin does not differ. These are members who have a special place in our heart.

Queen Ragnelf

Ragnelf is a calm and gentle woman who has seen her share of tragedies. After Ingirun died, the throne of Aesin went to her. Since then she has created a strong house out of the ashes of a war-torn family. Her kindness is widely known among members of House Aesin, and although she is well versed in most Arts, she realized a long time ago that her mind was her greatest weapon. During our recent travel from Alfheim to Midgard, she vanished without a trace, and the sadness she left us with is hard to bear.

High Lord Magnhildr

When Ragnelf vanished, this former member of the Council of Virtues took the throne and now acts as ruler of House Aesin. Unlike her predecessor, Magnhildr lacks

compassion. Some even call her "Iron Face" because of her stern looks. If her mind is firmly set on something, she will accept no further discussions. Although she is a strong leader, most members of our house fear that she will lead us to a new downfall.

Jarl Brondolf

The passion that this Unseelie Brondolf has is unmatched by most changelings. When he goes into battle, there are few who can withstand his powerful attacks. As a wilder in his prime years, he has his share of admirers, but ever since he took over the warrior training, he has become solemn and sad. With the recent leaving of Magnhildr, he was elevated to sit in the Council of Virtues, where he is the youngest member ever. We Volvas have seen in our visions that he is the one who will act as mediator between the Ancients and us.

Baron Bjorn

This baron was once a promising wilder on the verge of transcending into a grump, but the possession of mortal flesh became too much for him to handle. When commoners recently ambushed one of the first Aesin freeholds, he turned on us. House Aesin believes that the impurity of mortal flesh caused him to identify with the weaker commoner Kithain. If apprehended he will stand trial and face judgment so that this matter can be put to rest. Still, most members of the house pity him, and the childlings have begun to make rhymes about "Bjorn, the commoner lover."

Kin by Association: Urd, Verdandi, and Skuld

We know of them as the Norns. They are incredibly powerful beings, older than the oldest Ancient. They carry our blood, or so others say, and from time to time they visit us without warning. Urd, the keeper of the past, appears as a young maiden whose looks enchant every man on sight. Verdandi, weaver of the present, comes to us in all her motherly pride. She is the embodiment of a wilder Aesin. The oldest of the sisters, the crone, Skuld, is the one who holds the secrets of the future. When the Norns come, show your respect, for their agenda is incomprehensible to us. Usually they live in the Kingdom of Dán, and from their temple they weave our future. Will they act or will they stand aside when the final battle comes?

Pleasant Dreams

I can feel that you have to think about what you have learned here today. It's a heavy burden to belong to our proud house, but at the same time, find comfort that we are those who stand between total darkness and light. Leave now and sleep. I must attend to business of my own. We will see each other again . . . soon.

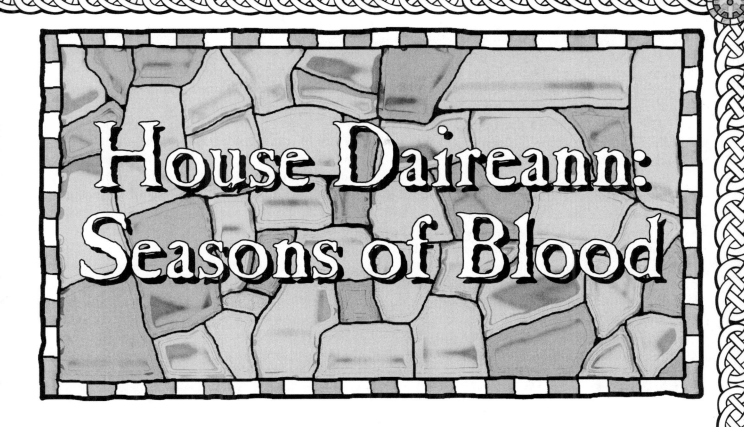

House Daireann: Seasons of Blood

Fire they cried
So evil must die.
And yields are good
So men pull back hoods and smile.
—XTC, "Sacrificial Bonfire"

Once upon a time, after a terrible storm in the Kingdom of White Sands, a lord of the fae rescued a lady of that ilk from a windswept beach. When she had recovered, they vowed to share their stories. The lord told his tale first so that the lady might refresh herself with meat and drink. He showed her his forge and his manor, and her eyes drank the beauty therein. Finally, she began her own tale:

So, what have you heard of our house, young Dougal lord, if you have heard of us at all? I imagine the story might start something like this. . . .

Their throats parched with war lust, the hearts of these Celtic fae burn to hear the call of battle. Every chance to show prowess in combat is gladly seized with a nigh-berserker fury. Yet their great pride and unbending sense of honor prevents House Daireann members from becoming mad dogs. This is a band of fae, many sidhe and a few commoners, who call themselves Unseelie but in many ways combine the best and worst of the two courts.

Hah! That's the way we might be billed by some foppish herald. It says little of who we of House Daireann really are. You found me, alone and lost on that beach, and you have taken me graciously into the hospitality of your home. I owe you much for this, for we treat such trust and accord with deep respect. For that reason, and because I am tired of keeping my few memories to myself, I will tell you of House Daireann and of my life. You must also help me improve my speech habits; yours are so less stiff and formal than my own.

I am called Dearbhal ní Ruadh Dara, and my birth-place, as far as I know, was the land near Meath in the east of Eire. I know not whether the place still exists. More than I can say has changed since I departed, and my head aches from dipping into the well of memory. This land of America, to which I have newly come, is an odd place, and it is more strange that I now wear this human husk to cloak my true self. But if it is necessary to survive, then I shall partake of its warmth.

'Tis sorry I am that you have no fire, for this tale I spin would be better for one. But never mind that. I have told stories in far worse places and on darker nights than this. Far darker.

The Founding Tale

There'll be stories of great slaughter
and the crying of great queens.
There'll be mangling of wounds
And mounds made of the slain.
—Fergus, *Táin bó Cuailnge*

All talespinners of Celtic blood, human or fae, no doubt have tales about the deeds of great Fionn MacCumhail, and we are no different. Once upon a time, in the age of myth and legend, Fionn and his band of Fianna came to the lands of Bobh Dearg in Munster. Bobh Dearg himself was the son of the Dagda and a great hero in his own right. Moreover, he had two beauteous daughters, Daireann and Sadbh. Fionn's eyes lit on them both, but it was to Daireann he first laid open his heart. Daireann was not a wanton for his trifling, though. She insisted that if Fionn wanted her so badly, he must first promise to be faithful and true to her for a full year, forsaking all others. The crude bastard would have none of it, and Daireann's heart broke. She felt the pain all the

worse when Fionn then wooed Sadbh, a woman less set in her ways who would put up with any nonsense from Fionn, provided they could sate their lust together.

Daireann knew she must avenge herself on Fionn; he had insulted her honor and her love by his cruel actions. So she brewed a remarkable draught and saw that the hero drank it in his mead. Almost immediately he went mad, so much that the Fianna forsook their leader. It was Sadbh who finally cured him, but Daireann cared not. She had taken Fionn's measure and hopefully taught him a lesson. It is true, I must admit, that he was a good deal more kindly to Sadbh thereafter, she being the one who bore his son, Oisin.

This tells you something of Daireann and her ways, but how did she come to be the founder of a great fae house, one known for battle, not venom? Well, as skilled as she was at making poisons, so too was Daireann a great brewer of healing potions. There was once a high king of the fae named Adwyr ap Gwydion, and he had a goutish foot that no physic could cure. Daireann made a poultice for the king and his pains healed quickly, much to the astonishment of the entire court. In gratitude, Adwyr granted Daireann lands and a house title, noting that henceforth her heirs should bear the arms of *per pale vert and argent*, an oak tree counterchanged, symbolic of life, strength and protection. Obviously, the other fae present remarked dryly, the king had not heard of her trickery of poor Fionn. No one could have been more surprised by the honor than Daireann herself; she knew good and well that while an act of kindness, this healing deed was not worth granting her the status of founding a noble house. Perhaps for this reason, she was determined to *make* herself and her family and followers more than deserving of the accolade.

A House Divided

Although we Daireann do not often discuss it, there are indeed two distinct factions in our house. The largest and most prominent group consists of warriors. They generally decide the house policies, and the righ or ban-righ are nearly always from this faction. The smaller but no less powerful group is made of Daireann who are more bent toward magic, herbalism and, indeed, the brewing of potions both foul and fair. They must show some skills in war, as all members of the house do, but once their

Fior-Righ is complete, they are generally left to their own devices. This faction is particularly attuned to nature, and while they are certainly capable of using cantrips, many of their most powerful (and most foul) brews are the products of the natural world rather than the Dreaming and Glamour. For now, there is almost complete harmony between the two groups. As we enter a world much stranger and harsher than the one we left, I fear relations may deteriorate rapidly and nastily, particularly if some of the better-established houses try to use House Daireann's skills to gain an advantage in this war.

Growth of the House

Daireann herself was not much of a warrior and knew it would be hard to prove the house's worth in the most visible way, on the battlefield. Some say she was skilled with the bow and sling, but that is stretching things a bit. The true growth of our house, with our founder's blessing, came with the birth of Daireann's son, Conchobhair. No one knew who the boy's father was; his mother simply appeared one day with a babe-in-arms. But whoever Conchobhair's sire may have been, he endowed his son with giantish vigor, unflagging endurance and inhuman agility. It was Conchobhair who devised the Fior-Righ customs and the Three Laws by which we live: Honor, Vengeance and Hospitality. While the Escheat and Seelie and Unseelie codes *are* important, the teachings of Conchobhair supercede any other tenets of behavior, as far as we are concerned. I cannot begin to recount the battles he fought and the foes he slew single-handedly— hoards of redcaps, brutal wyrms and even some of our greatest foes, the Fomorians. I needn't tell you, I suppose, that his bravery and honor provided the central pillar of strength and visible power our house needed. Those who had been House Daireann in name now had a purpose and a cause: the thrill of war. I doubt any Gwydion king or queen had more fanatically devoted followers than did our greatest ard-righ. We never turned our faces away from any challenge he gave and rallied to whatever task he asked of us.

It is said that Conchobhair lived long enough to see the coming doom, the fall of the fae during the Sundering and Shattering. He didn't go to Arcadia but instead stayed on earth. His fate remains a mystery, but rest assured, as a house united we will seek word of his whereabouts—once we fathom the strange ways of this brand new world, that is.

The Three Laws

Thanks to the teachings of Conchobhair, son of Daireann, three laws reign supreme even over the Escheat and the Seelie and Unseelie Codes in our House:

Honor: Above all other things, honor is most important to House Daireann. But we define honor in many ways: keeping one's word, spurning cowardice or serving a cause are just a few examples. No one would ever want to be branded as a dishonorable cur, and, to put it bluntly, death would be a better prospect than such shame. To further complicate matters, one's *individual* honor is actually even more important than allegiance to one's liege. Many a Daireann hero has given bonds of fealty a pass when it came to preserving his or her personal honor. This is one of several reasons why House Daireann is known as Unseelie.

Vengeance: House Daireann has a bloodthirsty reputation, thanks to this tenet. Usually, no amount of material recompense is sufficient to satisfy an insult or ill treatment. A duel or battle is often the only solution. Moreover, the vengeance is usually quick and brutal. Fae of our house like dueling, particularly of the Danse Macabre sort. When our ire is roused, House Daireann makes vengeance a true art.

Hospitality: Members of my house will never deny anyone shelter, even a foe, when honorably asked. Any denials gain the Daireann a bad reputation and a stamp of dishonor. The host should be prepared to give quality fare to his guests, not the leavings of his table (nor the poisons of his larder). Being a good host does have reasonable limits, though. Daireann hosts claim the right to ask for entertainment and stories in return for our hospitality, as well as the reasonable expectation of some day receiving hospitality in return from our visitors.

More on Vengeance

A tiny minority of House Daireann members aren't above the Dance of Iron (see p. 245 of **Changeling: The Dreaming**). However, there are some fae of House Daireann, often the women of Belladonna's Chalice (see "Secret Societies"), who specialize in producing and administering exquisitely complex and deadly poisons. Some of these may take weeks to kill an enemy, painfully at that. Those who give House Daireann reason to wreak vengeance on them sometimes get more than they deserve.

History

I knew by the voice of the battle crow over your dun every evening,
Since you went from me comely and terrible,
That misfortune and grief were at hand.
—Ailne in Lady Gregory's *Gods and Fighting Men*

The Mythic Age

Is there a one of us who does not wish for that half-remembered past? It was our time; the world was our world. In noble courts we were prized healers and masters of herbal lore; our warriors were champions to kings and peerless on the field. Our skill and valor inspired mortals throughout the Celtic lands of Scotland, Wales, Ireland, Brittany, Cornwall and the Isle of Man to tell tales and practice Arts that enriched the world with Glamour. Those many tribes, as well as the peoples before them, learned from us, fought with and against us and became mighty and dauntless warriors.

The Sundering

As the bonds between this world and the next weakened, battles became less epic but more desperate. Our swords were seldom bright in those days, for blood—fae and mortal alike—was spilled more frequently. But though our banner was feared on the battlefield, the oaken standard was a welcome sight when flying over a manor or lodge, for it guaranteed an evening's worth of food and shelter, even if it meant a night on the cold ground for the host.

The Shattering

We are not a house of seers and seldom quest for foreknowledge beyond the outcome of the next battle. The coming of the Shattering was a surprise to us. But as trod crumbled and freehold faded, our few holdings quickly filled with refugees. I am proud to say our house was not in the vanguard of the retreat to Arcadia. Many among Conchobhair's followers insisted that they be the last to leave, letting griffins, lions and dragons take to the trods first. Some members waited too long. Others, perhaps, stayed of their own accord, our lord Conchobhair among them.

The Interregnum

I know nothing of this time. Those of our house who stayed behind have vanished; we honor their memories as we search for some hint of their fate. I see the claws of Banality have lengthened and sharpened since our departure, and I feel them biting my own flesh. Even brave deeds and honor could not have fought off such an enemy forever. I am just grateful that we few who have returned have managed to do so safely. There is so much we don't understand, and we have so little time to become accustomed to what is strange and unfamiliar.

I know you are wondering whether I remember any details of the exodus from Arcadia. I would tell you if I did, certainly, but nothing is clear anymore. All I recall is the biting cold here. I am sorry things have taken such a turn for the worse in these lands. We had hoped to find a better place where instead we find fading dreams and a world that has by and large forgotten us.

The New Resurgence

It maddens me that I recall so little of our return to this world. The journey was long, this much I remember. But you wish to know why we left, don't you? Not for any disgrace, I assure you—death would have been the price of that, whether another's or ours. But the most clear sighted of us speak of a grimness, like the howl of a distant war horn or the frigid dimness that heralds a blizzard. I doubt not that we came here to defend against an ancient foe. But do we fight to protect the Autumn lands, or is Earth the battleground before Arcadia's gates? This I do not know.

Who is this ancient foe? Why, 'tis the Fomorians, those whom we last battled in the ancient times before the Sundering. I see you are scoffing, that you have bought into the purely Seelie myth that they will be easily vanquished. Well, I can tell you that they are old, cruel and terrible. House Daireann is all for striking now, before they are completely empowered, but as they are still in Arcadia, just waiting for a chance to assault this world, I'm not sure how a preemptive strike might work. It infuriates me that you who have been here for some years take this foe less seriously. There will come a day when you rue your words, I fear.

The Throes of War

For now, though, I suppose you *do* have some more pressing matters. This impending war you speak of, we would be honored to serve on the side of the noble cause. I respect many commoners, truly I do, but their place is at the right hand of the sidhe, not sitting on their thrones! I pity any who think the common folk can have some sort of fair and equal rule with the sidhe. No wonder your Ard-Righ David lost his throne! Perhaps if he is found, he will have learned that the old ways are the best ways.

Society

May the seven terriers of hell sit on the spool of your breast and bark in at your soul-case.

—Ancient Celtic curse

Recently, before my unfortunate adventure that brought me to your hold, I went to a place called a buffet. Marvelous concept! Almost like the legendary Cauldron of Plenty! The buffet is much like the conventions of House Daireann society. We pick and choose our rules from the Unseelie and Seelie codes, the tenets of the Shadow Court and the Escheat. But we first follow the Laws of Conchobhair. Our take on life is no more complex than this, my friend. But I see you want some details, so let me elaborate.

Growing Up in House Daireann

I admire the way your Dougal childlings learn an art or skill. Our young ones learn much, too, albeit in the realm of war rather than peace. Let me explain.

The Chrysalis

We greet the coming of new Kithain into our midst with joy. The awakening of a fae during Chrysalis confirms the turning of the seasons and the renewal of the cycle. Only one event can dampen the spirits of those in attendance at such a wonderful event: when the new changeling comes unto herself with a physical blemish in her fae mien, for this means she can never be ban-righ, or righ in the case of a young man.

Simply put, we do not allow our righ or ban-righ to have visible disfigurements of the flesh. Rightly or wrongly, we believe that disfigurement of the body indicates potential unworthiness on the field of war, and our high lords must set an example on the battlefield. Such rules do not apply to anyone other than the high king or queen. Indeed, since our brief time back on earth, a number of our house members have willingly tattooed their flesh with marks of the Celts. Surely you have seen those who wear spirals and knots almost anywhere they have skin to dye? A few have even gone so far as to have the chirurgeons change their human bone structure to make it more like their original fae appearance. I myself can survive without my usual ears, but others cannot. I suppose it makes them feel more at home in their human body. Yet I see that this practice of intolerance toward imperfection in our rulers shocks you, and I am sorry, for we value our friendship with Dougal.

Fostering

One of the most important times in the young Daireanns' life is the time of fostering. Our families never rear their own children. Instead, they send them into the homes of others of our lineage to learn proper behavior and, most importantly, skills of arms. Competition is stiff to have a childling taken into the dwellings of the best warriors, and usually there are tests the young fae must overcome to be accepted. Never fear, though, for we always find a safe and prosperous place for the childlings to grow up. What sorts of things do they learn? Well, they are trained in war from the first days of their fostering, and by this I mean they start at the very beginning. I remember that I worked for months in the stables of my lord, cleaning stalls and lifting bales of hay before anyone ever spoke to me of combat. Gradually, my strength and endurance improved. Only after a year was I permitted to heft a sword, and even then it was made of wood. Things are done precisely in our training, one step at a time.

Along with the physical training, we learn of tactics and, of course, the stories and traditions of our house, particularly the teachings of Conchobhair. And we hear about the Escheat and Seelie and Unseelie codes. Most of us learn a craft of some sort, even if we're not very good at it, poor indeed compared to one of House Dougal. I know a little of repairing weapons, enough to be of some use in war. Others may choose weaving, jewelry making or whatever interests them. Some also choose to learn, as Daireann did, the art of making potions with many purposes. Rest assured that there are none of her skill still alive.

Saining

Most childlings stay in fosterage for several years, but at the end of the first year and a day, they have their Saining ritual. It is actually quite a minor event, usually attended by the childling's foster family and perhaps a great lord or lady who confirms the young one's True Name. There is a small celebration, then things go right back to normal. For us, seeing as how all of House Daireann are sidhe, save for a few adopted commoners, the *real* event to watch is the Fior-Righ.

Fior-Righ

Unlike most other houses, in Daireann the Fior-Righ is a time of challenge, the passage into adulthood usually given when the childling becomes a wilder, rather than at Saining. All members of House Daireann who would call themselves warriors run a gauntlet of sorts in the presence of the local ranking lord or lady. Any available warriors are welcome to participate. They let their interest be known, and the new wilder has to best them in a fight. Ah, but it is not so simple! The would-be warrior must fight each challenger in turn to a battle of first blood. As long as she wins every fight, from every challenger, all is well. However, should she lose a fight, she must begin again with the first challenger. Thus, a Fior-Righ can go on for hours or days. The weapons are chimerical, but the fatigue and stress is not! I should also point out that the crux of the test is not in winning every fight easily. No, the local noble and his council *really* want to see how the new warrior comports herself in battle. Is she brave? Honorable? Stalwart? Does she know how to pace herself? I would say that few, if any, warriors have bested every challenger on their first try. Usually, the noble calls a halt after he has seen enough to make judgment, after a few hours. Then, assuming the news is good, the celebrations commence. This is the moment a young fae truly knows she is part of a long and glorious heritage.

The Codes of Conduct

As I explained, some of our views on behavior set us clearly outside the Seelie court, and we have accepted an Unseelie mantle though it is not a perfect fit. As is our nature, of course, we change according to what moods suits us, and many of our house follow the old customs of remaining Unseelie from Samhain to Beltaine and Seelie the rest of the year. But even before the Shattering, this practice was falling somewhat out of favor. It is impossible to say what every Daireann fae thinks of the codes, but here are some of my individual thoughts.

The Unseelie Code

Change is Good.

This is true chiefly because stagnation is bad. If we never changed, how could we continue to be effective warriors? For myself, I know that I will train and hone my skills for the rest of my days. Any fae who thinks that change is for ill is a fool.

Glamour is Free.

Why should it be otherwise? Are we not survivors? And is not Glamour one thing essential to our well-being? I will take what I need to endure, and I daresay most others would say the same thing!

Honor Is a Lie.

On the other hand, I can't agree with other Unseelie on this. What matters is how you *define* honor, and that is a completely personal and individual thing. Therefore, it is not a falsehood if you know in your own heart what honor means.

Passion before Duty

Well, I say this depends on where your duty lies. If passion is necessary (and it often is) to drive an army under my command to victory, so be it. I would do anything to light the fires necessary to rouse my warriors. Thus, passion and duty become one. If, however, you are speaking of lust or drooling over some song or poem while there is work to be done, passion be damned.

The Seelie Code

Death before Dishonor

Yes, I agree completely with this tenet. Without honor, we are nothing, no better than worms crawling on the earth. Honor is one of the three greatest things we treasure, and I would much rather be dead by iron than lose my honor.

Love Conquers All.

This sounds like a load of Fiona horse dung to me! Love is powerless when there is an iron dagger sticking in your heart. It's as simple as that.

Beauty Is Life.

There is nothing beautiful about a battlefield covered in blood, true enough, and the passing of life is ugly. But sometimes a greater beauty comes through loss, or at least a deeper appreciation for what you have. I would say we could not appreciate life or beauty without feeling the pain of death and ugliness first.

Never Forget a Debt.

Conchobhair spoke well when he wove together the themes of honor and hospitality into the laws. To forget a debt owed to another is dishonorable in the extreme, just as those who owe you should keep their promises as well.

The Shadow Court

Understand the Mortal World.

Although I love and seek the Glamour of mortals as much as any fae, I never gave the process of *understanding* them much thought until now. In this new world, it seems, mortals are more powerful than ever before. If knowing their ways is a requirement for taking Glamour, then we will do what is necessary.

Understand the Supernatural World; Make and Break Alliances as Necessary.

Isn't this the most important secret of survival? If we do not know our friends and enemies well, then we are doomed. Perhaps I have not spoken much of it, but even though we are warriors, we take time to learn a bit about our foes and allies alike. This is just a part of our tactics.

Harvest Glamour; Prepare for Endless Winter.

Hmmm. Having full stores in time of war is wise. I am not yet convinced of the coming Winter, though. Nor am I particularly afraid if it does come. Isn't this just part of life's cycle?

Overthrow the Seelie Court and Nobility.

Maybe they need overthrowing and maybe they do not. As I said, I am sure your Ard-Righ David meant well, even if he was misguided. We as a rule have tended to pay more attention to our local kings and queens than the high ones anyway, and that goes for following their orders as well as overthrowing them.

Fulfill the Ritual Obligations of the Year, Culminating in Samhain.

This is a must. We see the year and, indeed, life itself, as an endless cycle of seasons. War turns to peace, and peace turns to war, just as winter, spring, summer and fall follow each other every turn of the year's wheel. Marking the ritual holidays is simply part of our acceptance of the cycle.

Spread Chaos, Revolution and Anarchy.

Chaos keeps things lively. If there is always something going on, you do not have time to be lazy and complacent. And revolution works much the same way. Anarchy, on the other hand, seems to be too extreme. Order in battle is a good thing; wars would be lost without some type of structure.

The Escheat

The Right of Demesne

As I said before, we do give homage as is due to the high king or queen of a given realm. But the people who have our strongest loyalties are those closest at hand, the rulers of local strongholds. If they are good rulers and have proven themselves such, we will defend their right of sovereignty to the death. If they are shoddy, then we might just be the ones removing them from their estates.

The Right to Dream

We would be insane to constantly and cruelly drain mortal after mortal of their Glamour. Eventually, there would be no one left! Of course they have the right to dream in peace. But by the same token, we have a right to take Glamour if we need it. As a general rule, I dislike Ravaging, but should we be in a life or death struggle, I would be the first to take Glamour from a mortal, by force if necessary. Survival is still one of my strongest instincts.

The Right of Ignorance

Well, yes, the fact that we exist should ideally be kept secret. But sometimes, it is simply impossible! Those of us who are newly returned have not yet adapted as well as you who have been here for some decades. This is a perilous time for us newcomers, and if we make some errors, the rest of you will have to be understanding.

The Right of Rescue

Unquestionably, any fae who are in danger must be saved, even if we must defy our leaders' orders not to do so. This is part of my personal code of honor. I care not if the endangered person is enemy or friend. Some things transcend love and hate, and being imprisoned by Banality is such a thing.

The Right of Safe Haven

I am still stunned that there are so few havens of the Dreaming left— 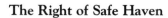 at least that is what I have observed in my short time here. The discovery of freeholds and other places of power is not the strong suit of our house. However, we would always give aid if asked to protect any realm of Glamour against Banality.

The Right of Life

To fear death is natural for any being. I understand this. But I also believe that we return to life, perhaps in a year, perhaps a thousand years. This is part of the endless cycle. I know such beliefs are not held by most other sidhe; this is why they abhor death so much. We of House Daireann do not have the same terror of dying, at least not so deeply. For that reason, we are less squeamish about death in battle. It is ugly, true, but sometimes it is also a necessity. This harsh truth is something we learn from the day after our Saining.

The House Blazon

House Daireann's blazon is *per pale vert and argent*, an oak tree counterchanged. (An oak tree half pale green, half silver centers the shield with its green half shown against the silver background, its silver half shown against the green). The blazon symbolizes all the qualities held most dear by Daireann: strength, life and protection, Unlike Liam's blazon, this oak tree is in full leaf, vibrant with life.

House Boon and Ban

Battlewise: House Daireann members are among the fiercest and most stalwart of all fae warriors. The difficulty of the Dragon's Ire is always lowered by 1 for members of this house, even if this exceeds the −3 cumulative modifier. Also, they will not flee in combat unless ordered to do so by the ranking war leader (and even then, they'll be the last people off the field).

Loose Tongue: House Daireann fae can't keep a secret to save their lives, literally, and stories of these *lapsus lingua* abound through Celtic legends. They're the ones who, in a series of wild brags, explain the one way they can be killed, probably to the wrong person, or share the intimate details of any Geas they're under. Anytime a fae of House Daireann boasts of her deeds (not an uncommon occurrence), she must roll Willpower with three successes to avoid blabbing some secret. Note that House Daireann fae *don't* go spilling the beans to complete strangers, although with a little work, a clever stranger can become a friend.

Holidays

As I have said, our yearly holidays are quite important. They mark the passage of days and allow us to remember traditions of ages gone by. Also, those few among us who do dabble in sorcery and potion brewing find that working their Arts on these days seems to garner the most potency.

Samhain (October 31 and November 1)

We use this holiday not to play insane tricks or engage in raucous depravity, but rather to think about the dead and departed, honoring our Celtic ancestors. It is also a time for exchanging gifts and bringing in the final bounties of harvest. And like on all our holidays, we light *teanlas*, or bonfires, to symbolize the Balefires and our respect for Glamour and the Dreaming.

Alban Arthan (December 21)

This holiday marks the coming of winter. Like mortals, we give gifts, but the biggest event of the day is an enormous feast. The cooks spare no expense for this celebration, and included in many of the dishes are interesting magical trinkets or bits of hard-to-find ingredients for working cantrips.

Imbolc (February 2)

We celebrate Imbolc much as do other fae. It is actually a day of resting, as far as we are concerned, a time for wearing bright colors and sitting around the fire with friends and family.

Alban Eilhir (March 20)

This is the day of vernal equinox, when the day is half in light, half in shadow. Not too much happens other than some games of chance, friendly dueling and the traditional eating of plums—plum pie, plum pudding, plum wine, you name it.

Walpurgis Night and Beltaine (April 30, May 1–2)

Walpurgis Night is a rather active evening for the Unseelie. Since our old traditions hold that the Seelie will take their thrones on Beltaine, there is often a pretty rowdy celebration on April 30. On Beltaine, we eat oatcakes and burn fires made of oak in honor of Daireann. And there's also the maypole dance around a birch pole topped with colorful ribbons. You are familiar with this, I am sure. Dancers weave among each other with the ribbons, "braiding" the maypole. Sometimes a male fae is bound to the pole, reminiscent of the ancient sacrifice some high kings used to make to preserve the sanctity of the land. It is considered a mark of esteem and honor if you are the one asked to stand in the high king's place.

Alban Hefin (June 21)

This is the summer's birth, and we usually stay up the entire day and night, celebrating the wild beauty of the outdoors. Most childlings like to make paper chains, which we then burn in a great bonfire during the evening.

Lughnasadh (August 1)

The first of August is Lughnasad, marking the gradual end of the summer and the beginning of harvest. We wear earth tones on this day and eat bread baked from the first dainty grains plucked from the fields. It is a time for somewhat more sober contemplation of the waning of one cycle and the beginning of another

Alban Elfed (September 23)

Alban Elfed, like the spring equinox, is a day of balance, when light and dark are equal. It marks the spiral of the year toward Samhain and is a time for gathering and consuming fruits of the harvest.

Secret Societies

You asked me whether House Daireann has any secret societies, but I am not sure what you mean by that. We have some groups of like-minded fae who have banded together for common interests, but I would not exactly call them secret. Are you trying to tell me there are covert factions in most houses? I had no idea!

Belladonna's Chalice

The members of this order are usually women, though there is no requirement as such. They meet on each change of the season and plan out their schedule of brewing for the coming months. If any dare say that the members of this society are less worthy because they have skill in their heads rather than their muscles, I'd call them liars. Like all sidhe of our house, those of Belladonna's Chalice, too, have passed the Fior-Righ. They are extremely clever and probably know more of herbalism, healing and poison than any of your modern physics. I am not sure of the exact requirement for membership, but I believe it has something to do with concocting a unique brew and demonstrating to the present members how it can be used. Most members freely admit their association and generally are quite pleased to work for barter.

The Companions of the Oaken Cudgel

While Conchobhair was quite the swordsman, one of his most underestimated weapons was his oaken staff. Hewn from a single oak tree's heart, the staff was over 7 feet in length, and some even say its base was shod in iron. In memory of Conchobhair, House Daireann holds dear a group of oathbonded fae calling themselves the Companions of the Oaken Cudgel. Members gain admittance only by invitation. They must prove themselves masters of three weapons, one of those being the cudgel, of course. But most important, the members exemplify Conchobhair's Three Laws, holding honor highest of all. It is quite a privilege to be invited to join the Companions, and I have never known of any to refuse the call.

Stewards of Cauldronhouse

Hospitality, as you know, is one of the three pillars of our law code. If the Companions of the Oaken Cudgel symbolize honor, as the members of Belladonna's Chalice do vengeance, then the Stewards of Cauldronhouse are the standard bearers of hospitality. They put service to others before their own needs. Even dire enemies of House Daireann can rest in peace, for the requisite three days at least, without any fear of betrayal or revenge.

Oaths of House Daireann

Oath breaking is an unthinkable breach of honor in House Daireann, and those who take oaths do so solemnly and for life. Should a Daireann break an oath, it would only be because a greater matter of honor had demanded it. Usually, an oath is sworn on some type of weapon, and, almost always, a gentle bloodletting is part of the ceremony.

Oath of the War Band

The most feared of the House Daireann warriors are those who have sworn an oath to form a war band. Those entwined within such an oath circle fight for one another's lives and honor, no matter what may come to pass. They are single minded and unbending in their protection of and loyalty to one another. Daireann bards sing many long laments about how certain of these bands have been slain, one by one, until the last remaining warrior takes his own life rather than stand alone on the battlefield. The would-be band clasps wrists and stands in an unbroken circle to recite the oath, stated as follows:

Brothers and Sisters, by the edge of the sword and the bond of blood do I swear the strength of my arms and the courage of my heart to defend you and our cause from the might of our foes. Never shall you stand alone on the battlefield as long as breath remains in my body. Should I break my oath, may a rain of cold iron daggers pierce my breast and send my soul forever into darkness.

Then, each fae makes a cut on her palm and in turn grasps the palm of all other members of the war band. The oath is then in effect. Thenceforth in battle, when fighting as part of a unit, each member has 1 extra point of Willpower to be used only in the combat. Additionally, under the same conditions, all members gain 1 extra Bruised health level. Both the Willpower point and the extra health level fade at the end of the combat, which can lead to dire consequences to the Daireann who fights on beyond his normal health levels.

Even our law of vengeance cannot supercede the granting of hospitality by the Stewards. Of course, there is no rule that those seeking vengeance cannot wait out their enemies on a nearby road. . . . Anyway, the Cauldronhouses—oh yes, there are many of them, or at least there used to be—are scattered around the various lands, often at crossroads. You can tell one by the standard of House Daireann flying on a pole topped by a miniature cauldron. It is a happy sight for a tired soul, I assure you.

Relations with Other Houses

I am certain you wish to know how we get along with other houses, yours included. Like most fae, we have our friends . . . and our enemies.

House Aesin

They lack subtlety, but damn, what a fine sight in battle! They have many of the old and honored customs that we do, and for that we generally count them as allies. If they have a flaw, it is their one-sided view of everything. It is hard to get an Aesin to compromise or give in on anything, but that is not necessarily a disadvantage when the enemy is bearing down on you.

House Ailil

Perhaps they have a poor reputation in some quarters, but we find those of House Ailil to be worthy nobles, clever and battle wise. Should the tide of war come, they would make valiant leaders. In the olden days, I believe it was most often the sidhe of this house who wore the mantles of the righ and ban-righ when summer turned to winter. We wouldn't be sorry to see those days return.

House Balor

We find the Balor despicable. Their very founding is rooted in dishonor and lies. They flaunt their darkness, so evident in their twisted bodies. As far as we are concerned, they have nothing to offer. The call themselves Unseelie but have no true grasp of what that honestly means. Instead, they are content to wallow in petty plots, never lifting a finger to aid their fellows. Would that they had stayed behind in Arcadia!

House Beaumayn

Many years ago, so we hear, warriors of this house journeyed east to what was called the Holy Land and no doubt learned many tactics of war that would have been of great interest to us. Unfortunately, we never found out much about what they learned; when the Beaumayn returned, they were no longer stout warriors but mystics and prophets. We have had less to say to them since— and not only because of their strange embrace of cold iron. Quite frankly, soothsayers give me the chills; you can never tell when one is being truthful or just trying to goose you for his own amusement.

House Dougal

We have had some disagreements over the centuries, but we count Dougal among our strong allies. You understand the feelings of honor imbued in work well done, and in our stores of weapons, there have been many bearing the sigil of your house and its artisans. I hope that our bonds of friendship can be reforged into something even stronger in the coming days.

House Eiluned

Members of House Daireann have widely varying opinions on the Eiluned, so it depends on whom you talk to. Most of our warriors find them too scheming and caught up in devious intrigues, but those ladies and lords of Belladonna's Chalice have old friendships and alliances with House Eiluned. Now that we have returned to this world, perhaps our bonds with them will be stronger than before.

House Fiona

What a pack of fools to be distracted by all that romantic nonsense! Of course we are creatures of passion, and I can fall in love as easily as the next person, but the Fiona take things much too far. They could rank among the finest warriors of all if they did not lay abed so often. They have no sense of discipline and a poor grasp of duty. I wish it were otherwise, but I doubt these swooning romantics will ever change.

House Gwydion

The valiant warriors of House Gwydion are in actuality a lighter reflection of House Ailil, whether they would ever admit it or no. Yet I find them too optimistic; they have trouble facing the reality of how things *should* be, well evidenced by the misadventures you describe of your Ard-Righ David. However, we of House Daireann admire their sense of honor. Perhaps in the coming war they will learn to temper their gentler ways.

House Liam

Maybe there is a story behind it, but as we understand it, Liam fae are oath breakers. How can we trust people without honor? I would not deny them hospitality, and it is interesting how much they love mortals, but I generally find them distasteful. They are simply not the kind of people we tend to find enjoyable.

House Scathach

Their belief in commoner equality aside, they are some of the best among us. We have been known to scrap and argue, it is true, but I would rather have an enemy Scathach at my back than a Balor ally at my side. I know there are some, ah, unpleasant rumors floating around that tell of a Daireann betrayal of the Scathach, but, really, none of us remembers too much of what has happened before. Truly!

House Varich

These fae who stand on the shores of the east and the west are oddly compelling, and I wish I knew more of them. Their warriors are valiant and their sorcerers wise and powerful. Occasionally, we have spoken with some from this house, but the secrets they have revealed are few and far between. So what do they want by returning to this world? They revel overmuch in darkness, and it is unclear to us why this is so.

Loose Lips: Of Scathach and Daireann

Any observer can see some interesting similarities between these two houses of Celtic extract. Both have a matrilineal tradition, a love for all things martial and deep respect for honor and bravery. So, why is it that things are, well, a little strained between these fae?

Most of the blame, sadly, falls upon the Daireann. Once upon a time, Scathach herself had a powerful student named Cú Chulainn. He had, as did many fae, a Geas laid upon him; he could not refuse hospitality should it be proffered. Unfortunately, the warrior was under the influence of *another* Geas so that he couldn't consume the flesh of a dog. The hero was in a very bad position indeed when offered a hospitable meal that included dog stew. That event more or less began the downfall of poor Cú Chulainn. Interestingly enough, those who concocted this accursed stunt received their information from the Morrigu, who was angered at Cú Chulainn. The Morrigu, in turn, heard it from some loose-lipped fae who probably meant no harm. While the specific blabbermouth is unknown, most Scathach are sure it was Finias, a Daireann companion of Cú Chulainn.

If that weren't enough to strain relations, some Scathach of Caledonia still bear a grudge for the capture of King Patrick of Dalriada by King Richard of Albion at the Battle of Neville's Cross in 1346. Supposedly, the Dalriadan monarch, a member of House Scathach, was traveling back to a border stronghold when he took refuge in the humble barn of an English mortal lord who'd seen better days. Given instructions to obtain bread and wine from the lord's larders, Seamus of House Daireann, a young squire, hastened to do his lord's bidding. Little did he know that a winsome satyr lass served the lord, too, and Seamus had the great misfortune to meet her in the scullery. She promised her help to the Scots fae, only to break her promise and get word to the court of King Richard. A battle ensued in the dawn, wherein King Patrick and all his forces were captured. He blamed Seamus's loose tongue, though the Daireann lad insisted that the satyr was the true villain. In any case, those of House Scathach look askance at the fae of House Daireann, admiring their courage but ever doubting their trustworthiness off the battlefield.

Views on Other Kith

As we have views on our fellow nobles, so do we on the other kith as well. I am uncertain how they would respond to our thoughts concerning them, but I will not lie to fit in with more popular, modern notions. We are what we are; we think as we think!

Commoners

House Daireann sidhe come from a time when commoners stayed more or less within their own oathcircles. There was certainly not animosity between the two groups of fae, and any commoner who asked for hospitality and comported himself with honor was accepted and welcomed. Some even served within the house as skilled crafters, yeoman or soldiers. However, things are *very* different in this brave new world. The Daireann *cannot* understand why commoners, particularly ones who are not war leaders, have so much political power. Why, they are even rulers of some territories! It is true that there are a few commoners in House Daireann, notably some trolls and sluagh. And they are appreciated but expected to keep their place. It is the sidhe, after all, who are supposed to be the rulers, and it's as simple as that. Any commoner who can live with this and other edicts of the house is most welcome. Any who cannot is shown the front door.

Boggans

Stalwart sorts, they know much of hospitality. And there are a few who have learned the way of the bow and arrow. While I would not necessarily count one as a close friend, they have their uses in times of peace.

Eshu

Eshu make wonderful guides, and the stories they tell are always exciting. But as a kith, they are too easily distracted. It is hard to get them to keep their minds to the business at hand. I am sure this eshu knight, this Seif you speak of, means well, but will he really accomplish what he sets out to do?

Nockers

Your own house well exemplifies the benefits of having nockers around. In war, we will gladly accept their companionship at our forges. Otherwise, though, I find them boorish and crude. Until they learn some manners, we will give what hospitality is necessary and not much more.

Pooka

These twisted liars are annoying in the extreme. Some find their tricks amusing, but I say these tricksters cannot be trusted. Their petty schemes to gain attention waste time and energy. I have yet to meet a pooka who impressed me.

Redcaps

Vicious, nasty bastards who, whether we like to admit it or not, occupy a unique place in Kithain society. That's right! If it were not for the redcaps, who would do all our dirty work? We have employed them from time to time, and with the proper authority, they can be unstoppable soldiers on the battlefield. Perhaps we would do well to remember this in the coming war.

Satyrs

One of the great heroes of our house, Finias, met his doom at the hands of a satyr temptress, who promised him and his lord safe passage only to betray them to the enemy. I know the satyrs' reputation is one of wisdom, but does knowledge necessarily impart honor? I think not.

Sluagh

A number of sluagh are close to our house, particularly with the Daireann in Belladonna's Chalice. They have served us well in the past, and we look forward to renewing those bonds of friendship and service in the present.

Trolls

Trolls are the finest among the commoners, and in some respects, I trust them more than I do certain nobles (certainly more than the wretched Balor). They are brave fighters and have a keen sense of honor that rivals our own. I have never known a troll to betray our trust.

Gallain, Prodigals and Others

My particular memories of others, the lost ones, are more vague than of our fellow Kithain. Here are some recollections I have from the misty times before the Shattering.

Nunnehi

The what? Oh, the native people of the Summer Lands. Well, the only thing I know of them has to do with the Legend of Prince Madoc of Cymru. Supposedly, he had some dealings with them, although relations were poor between the nunnehi and the fae in the prince's company. Other than that, I have not a clue about these folk.

Inanimae

We know far less of these creatures than do our fellows in House Varich, who are the true experts. I understand the Sessile Ones fell into a long sleep around the time of the Shattering. What their fate has been I have no idea, but with a coming war, it would be useful to rediscover these lost ones.

Thallain

We can be ruthless if the need calls for it, but I know the majority of House Daireann tends to avoid the Thallain if at all possible. They are rapacious and evil, having few if any redeeming qualities.

Fomorians

One reason we dislike the Thallain, incidentally, is that we are concerned that they might become allies of the greatest enemy of the Kithain, the Fomorians. No longer are they the stuff of forgotten legend, my friend. As I said earlier, we came back to this world when the opportunity arose to defend the mortal lands against these beasts. We will do what we must, though I warn you that this battle will be far worse than any we have ever faced.

Dauntain

As I said earlier, we hold great stake in the Right of Rescue. I find it sorrowful that your former Ard-Righ prohibited the fae from approaching the Dauntain. If they can be saved, or if they have taken others captive, we must take action, risks be damned. It is as simple as that.

Wizards

In the past, we tended to avoid the wizards, whose strange and bizarre magics were difficult to understand. I imagine we will do the same in the present, particularly if, as you say, they have magic steeped in machinery. We are too newly come to this world to take on an unknown enemy.

Ghosts

The ancient lands where we hail from are full of lost spirits. While we do not make a practice of seeking them out, they are to be pitied and aided if possible. Most are more annoying than dangerous.

Children of Lillith

Lillith's Children used to be a mixed lot of treachery, greed and an odd sort of honor, or so it seemed from the few dealings we had with them. They were best avoided, and that seems a sound practice to continue.

Mortals

I believe the lives and fates of the Kithain are forever interwoven with those of the Sons of Adam and Daughters of Eve. We count many relatives among the mortal kinain and not a few enemies among the Autumn People. As much as the Kithain, these humans are the ones we came back to save against the might of the Fomorians. We are not like the Liam, too caught up in the lives of mortals, but saving these innocents is a question of duty and honor.

Werewolves

I have met before with the shape changers and been friend to some. The Fenrir came to Eire as enemies long ago but became more like brothers as the years passed. And there are others, I am sure, whose names escape me. But there is one rabid band of the werewolves I *do* remember!

So, tell me, do those brothers of Fionn MacCumhail still wander this world? Bastards, the lot of them! They cannot see past a drink, a brawl or a one-night stand to make any kind of sense. Our enmity with the Fianna goes back a long way, and I daresay that is one thing we have not forgotten!

The Enmity of the Fianna

It should come as no surprise that enmity still exists between the Fianna and House Daireann. To the werewolves' minds, the house founder was an evil fae who rejected the amorous attentions of their greatest Kinfolk and poisoned him to boot! Fortunately for Daireann's descendents, most of the Fianna have forgotten all about the details behind the story, a tale that is still sung at moots. However, there may be a *few* among the Tuatha de Fionn camp with great knowledge of fae lore who *do* remember. It would be quite a nasty scene should such a pissy and well-informed Fianna meet a fae wearing the colors of House Daireann. . . .

Politics

Three things has a worthy noble: a groaning sideboard, a sleeping hound and a joyful voice.

—Ancient Celtic triat

Structures and Traditions

All that we believe and hold dear harks back to the Three Laws of Conchobhair. These teachings, while simple, are a powerful combination that has guided us since the Mythic Age. Other than adherence to these laws, the only other important tradition we have is the choosing of our rulers.

Choosing the Righ and Ban-Righ

It probably comes as no surprise that we choose our Righ and Ban-Righ in trial by combat. Our rulers reign until they lose a challenge, and challenges may be issued only on one of the four seasonal holidays, Imbolc, Samhain, Lughnasadh and Beltaine. A challenge must be accepted if it is given honorably. The only exception to this is if we are in the midst of war, when it would be folly to have a change in leadership. So, let us say, for example, that Righ Oisin became ruler on Beltaine. Come Lughnasadh, a young warrior named Niamh challenges him. The *comhairle*, a group of fae councilors who have been Righ or Ban-Righ before and are willing to serve as advisers, agree that she has given honorable challenge and has no physical marks that would disqualify her from rulership. Oisin and Niamh fight the best three out of five bouts, with *real* weapons of their own choosing, to first blood. If Oisin wins, he continues to be Righ until a new challenge comes, not before Samhain. If Niamh wins, she is immediately named Ban-Righ. The winner has the privilege of picking his or her own consort, usually a romantic attachment, but not always. In the case of multiple challenges, simple lot or perhaps a game of chance chooses the combatant, if the *comhairle* is so willing. It is a simple system and so far has worked well for us, and though you would expect every new holiday to bring a new ruler, it is not always so. If we are pleased with our Righ or Ban-Righ, several seasons may pass before a new challenger emerges. The fact that the ruler appoints all other territorial nobles and grants certain lands and titles may have something to do with this relative stability.

One thing that is puzzling is that during our recent coming to this world, we emerged with no Righ or Ban-Righ, only the presence of our Ard-Bantiarna, or high lady, as you would say, who is currently Fiadnait ní Strachan. This may have been because our Righ or Ban-Righ perished, or it might have been a condition of our return. In any case, I am certain that as soon as immediate matters are settled, Fiadnait will see to it that a Righ or Ban-Righ is chosen.

Political Leanings

Anarchists, Purists, Repudiators, Ritualists and Modernists? Other than their general meanings, which I can only guess, these terms are unfamiliar to me. I do not quite understand what you mean by political leanings.

Are these orders of warriors? As I have already said, we have a code of behavior, strict and simple, as dictated by Conchobhair. The Three Laws are all we really need to understand our house's political structure. Of course, I have no doubts that as the fae have changed, so too will some of our views on politics.

Movers and Shakers

You will hear some of these names soon enough, so let me take a moment to introduce you to some of the better-known members of our house who are newly returned to these lands.

Ard-Bantiarna Fiadnait ní Strachan

The position of "high lord or lady" is a concession to the desires of the other houses; whoever holds this job has come to be more like a chief steward than an actual ruler. She (or he) serves for life or until chosen retirement. A new high lord or lady is simply chosen by whomever is on the throne at the time of the former lord's or lady's demise or departure from office. Fiadnait is comfortably settled into her greybeard years now. In her youth, she gained a great deal of fame for slaying a dangerous chimera known as the Hound of the Black Isle, a foul creature that had plagued a Caledonian freehold for many years. In our recent days in this world, Fiadnait has tried to renew old alliances and find a stronghold for our house. Even though she is aging, with silver strands in her auburn tresses, she commands such respect that only a fool would challenge Fiadnait's authority. She is never without at least two weapons and not a few cantrips at her disposal. You can recognize Fiadnait by her cloak of office, a magnificent linen mantle with our house arms stitched in silken threads.

Eoghan ap Derryth

As I said earlier, only a few men belong to Belladonna's Chalice, and of those few, Eoghan ap Derryth is the most prominent. He is handsome in a lean, hawkish way, with a nose that has been broken once too often. Eoghan gave up the sword soon after his Fior-Righ and studied for years before gaining admission to the Chalice. No one knows exactly what kind of potion he brewed to join, but rumor has it that the extraction would give an imbiber immunity to the powers of cold iron. Surely that is impossible, but Eoghan has garnered quite a reputation. In the uncertain present days, no doubt he will be even more sought than before.

Iobhar and Sibéal

Iobhar and Sibéal are twins and important members of the Companions of the Oaken Cudgel. I have seen with my own eyes how unstoppable these two are! When fighting back to back, they can hold off nine times their number. Both, of course, are deadly with the cudgel. As far as other weapons, Iobhar uses the sword and poleax while Sibéal is mistress of the bow and spear. You seldom see one without the other, even at the sideboard. They are almost identical in looks, too, with long black hair and green eyes. I daresay one could not live without the other, and I hope that if they must one day fall, it is together rather than alone.

Ynyra ferch Nissian

I have already told you that we hold the trolls in high esteem. Just recently, one in particular gave us cause to honor her. This troll's name is Ynyra ferch Nissian, and as unlikely as it may seem, well do I recall what she did. Upon coming to these lands, the Fomorians unleashed a horror to try and stop our departure. I told you that they have powers that are not to be taken lightly! This beast took the form of a three-headed dragon, larger than one of your flying ships and spitting venom as deadly as cold iron. Many of our house flocked to defend the childlings from this creature, and several of our host fell trying to defend the young. Then Ynyra came forward and, with a single swipe of her great sword, she cleaved off one of the heads. The remaining heads attacked her again and again, giving the chance for those defenseless to escape and for our warriors to rally to Ynyra's side. By the time they arrived, she was nearly dead from bites and venom. Still, she sliced off another head before falling to her knees. Ten warriors finished off the beast, and those of Belladonna's Chalice at hand saved Ynyra. Such a battle under any circumstances would be cause for honoring her, but given the chaotic situation, she performed above and beyond the call of duty. I believe Ard-Bantiarna Fiadnait is going to ask our new Righ or Ban-Righ to honor Ynyra with a title, which is a *very* rare distinction for a commoner.

Treasures of House Daireann

House Daireann had at one time a number of magical Treasures stashed away for a time of great need. Alas, the Second Coming has erased many memories of these wondrous implements. Two Treasures that Ard-Bantiarna Fiadnait *does* hold, however, are the Cudgel of Conchobhair and the Cauldron of Sceanbh. They are priceless, and she hopes that once the Daireann are resettled, she can put these Treasures into the hands of a new Righ or Ban-Righ of the house. You look at me so strangely! Ah, I understand, you think I should not have told you this! Perhaps, yet now that I have done so, it seems a shame not to at least describe them!

The Cudgel of Conchobhair
(Unique Treasure, Level 4)

Conchobhair's cudgel is an unassuming oaken staff about 8 feet tall. It grants its bearer (and will only function for a member of House Daireann) several wonderful powers. The foot of the staff is shod in cold iron as a warning and, under the direst circumstances, as a possible weapon.

(The weapon inflicts Strength + 4 damage. The cudgel also adds +2 dice to any Kenning roll. Finally, anyone holding the staff receives 3 levels of Oakenshield usable for the battle she is currently involved in. Thus, if the user fights one opponent and is struck for 1 level, then goes on to another opponent and is struck again for another 2 levels, the Oakenshield is used up. The user must then face any other opponents without its benefit. On the other hand, should the user survive the first fight—with or without any levels of Oakenshield remaining—then engage in battle later that day, she would once again start the battle with 3 levels of Oakenshield. Such levels become usable once battle is joined, not simply as a consequence of carrying the weapon. If the user is ambushed and struck for damage, no levels of protection come into play until she actively turns to fight.)

The Cauldron of Sceanbh
(Unique Treasure, Level 4)

This cauldron has two functions, depending on the desires of the brewer. Its first power is to brew a potion that inspires warriors to great deeds. With an Intelligence + Kenning roll, with at least three successes, a brewer can make a potion that gives +1 to the Initiative roll of any imbiber; the warrior gains an additional +1 for every success over three the brewer has. The second power is more insidious. Again, it requires an Intelligence + Kenning roll with a minimum of three successes. This time, though, the potion is a powerful sleeping draught. Anyone who drinks it loses one die roll's worth of health levels per turn, with no Stamina roll allowed. Eventually, even the stoutest warrior will fall unconscious (though he may have time to take an action before succumbing to the potion). Such a potion could aid in healing or cause great suffering.

From Sir Hamish Somerled, to Princess Lenore of House Dougal, Good Greetings.

My liege, please find a disk enclosed with notes on a most unusual houseguest I've recently hosted. It seems that the intelligence reports are correct and that newcomers have indeed arrived from lost Arcadia. While the lady with whom I spoke had rather harsh views on the significance of physical appearance, we should also note with relish the edge of her sword. Could this indeed be, my Princess, the key you were looking for? I await your orders and remain your most devoted servant,

Hamish

House Varich: Patterns in Sunlight and Shadow

That's the future. You see, everything returns. . . .
—A pilgrim to the death site of the Romanov family,
In Siberia
The mist of the storm covers the sky,
The whirlwinds of snow are spinning;
Now, like a wild beast, it calls,
Now it cries, like a child
—Alexander Pushkin, "Winter Storm"

The History of House Varich

Sit. Make yourself comfortable by the hearth, young one. My name does not matter for the present. What matters is that you know the history of our house and the customs of your noble heritage. You belong to the lineage of Varich, the child of ancient and eternal powers and the embodiment of tragedy and nobility. Listen now, you who have newly come to this harsh and unforgiving world. I shall tell you all that you need to know to survive

and conquer. Though I, too, have only recently arrived, my memories have not faded as much as those of others like you. Do not worry; the past is important, but the future matters even more. Close your eyes and listen to my words as I build patterns in your mind. Hear now the history of the house of Varich, a tale that begins in the time of legends, when the powerful Vila, those whom other fae call the Tuatha de Danaan, fought the vicious Fomorians.

The Mythic Age

Long ago, before dreams were shattered, our founder, Varich, walked the northern lands. Varich was the bright and handsome son of Miesiac—known as the silver-haired, dark-eyed Moon—and Dazbóga the Sun, his proud mother, with golden braids coiling down to her feet and brilliant sapphire eyes.

No one could tell Varich anything he did not want to hear. From one moment to the next he fought, he loved and he laughed. Everyone was his friend, yet none caught Varich's heart. Neither delicate tsarevna nor lithe youth was good enough. None could best him in magic or war. None could match him in courage or passion. His parents despaired. Meeting in twilight one evening, they decided that they had waited long enough. First the Moon spoke to his servants, the spirits of the lake and mountains, commanding them to search for his son's perfect match.

Winds whistled in the highest reaches, seeking their goal in rocky crevasses and deep caves. Russalka spread their cold, clear, icy fingers wide. Trees rustled and shook as leshii climbed high in their branches, leaf-green eyes peering through taiga forests and among silver birches for the one who would capture the heart of Varich. Days and months passed. Nowhere could they find someone so perfect.

Varich's mother smiled. Dazbóga knew her son's love could not be found easily by the spirits. The Inanimae, though loyal, were not clever enough. She turned to the sluagh, those who seek the shadows made by her glory and find treasure hidden within. She placed a Geas upon them, vowing that they must search until the most perfect of all maidens could be brought to her son.

At first the sluagh despaired. Even the north wind, which travels to all places, could not find someone to satisfy Varich. How could the sluagh do better? Then the darkest and most crafty of them thought of a plan. In this day the sluagh were clever with their hands—weaving and fashioning magical treasures was as much their pleasure then as secrets and rot later became. Charodei, the sluagh sorceress, swore she could fashion a perfect mate for him, far better than any they could find in truth.

Though some feared Varich's anger if he discovered their trickery, the rest feared more the anger of his mother, the Sun. Charodei lied to the Moon and Sun, telling them a beautiful maiden, tsarevna of Lisaia, a kingdom to the south, longed to be Varich's bride. She boasted of the maiden's talents: her skill at battle, the way she rode a horse, her magical abilities beyond compare.

The Sun and Moon told Charodei to bring her quickly so that their son might look upon her. The sorceress smiled and whispered her promise to bring the beautiful one within three days. Returning to her dark, shadowy chambers, she began. With long, spidery fingers she sculpted a perfect body of snow and ice. She lovingly crafted graceful curves, slender legs and silky breasts. The snow maiden's eyes were fashioned of the clearest amber; her hair of gold, spun into fine flowing filaments; and her lips and the crown of her breasts stained with blood taken from the sorceress's very veins. Finally, all was ready, and to finish the spell she opened the breast of the icy beauty and placed within a ruby heart filled with the blood of mortals killed in the maiden's making.

The snow maiden stirred and sighed. Wrapped in soft sable as black as the shadows sluagh love, she was presented to Varich. Midnight eyes studied her as she dropped her gaze from him shyly. He was delighted with her beauty, thrilled with her seeming perfection. Impulsively Varich gathered her into his arms, his heart taken in an instant. Eagerly she returned his embrace, seeking his body as she was made to do. Passionate kisses led to further explorations. Charodei, however, had forgotten one vital flaw. As their bodies grew heated, as sweet tongues lapped at secret places and their limbs wrapped about each other, the snow maiden began to melt. Her amber eyes called to Varich beseechingly. Child of the Sun as he was, he watched helplessly as her beauty dissolved into a pile of slush tinged with the crimson of Charodei's blood. Varich's perfect lady disappeared beneath him, leaving in the end only a tangle of golden threads, a cracked and broken ruby stained with blood and the sable cloak in which she was wrapped. Varich cried out, his heart blackened and torn by the horror before him. Gathering a web of her golden hair in his hands, he vowed to never love another.

His parents were enraged. They began to search for Charodei, but, like most sluagh, she knew how to slip into the most hidden and slimy places. Finally they called a three-fold curse upon her and all her kind: She might never make nor have perfection; she would never see the light of the sun or moon without fear; and all others would know her for the treacherous creature she is.

Varich had no more heart to laugh, no more need for challenge or battle. He spent most of his time wandering through the bleakest parts of the Dreaming, speaking to no one. His hands were constantly busy, for as he wandered, his thoughts in darkness, he was fashioning a golden web from his lady's hair. Creatures of nightmare came forth from his dreams, yet he did not see them. Nothingness filled his mind. Still his hands moved, twisting the golden threads into patterns of sunlight and shadow.

It was during this time that he met another wanderer in the Dreaming. A strange creature came to him: Marena, she of snow-white skin, silvery tresses and icy garnet gaze. Lifting his face in her cold, long-nailed hands, she looked deep into his despairing midnight eyes. "Dear child of the Vila, what has brought you so far away from your place in the Dreaming? Why have you come to me?" she asked.

Looking at her, Varich did not know who or what she might be—could she be a fae lady from some unknown house sent by his parents? In her austere beauty, she reminded him of the maiden who filled his thoughts. He smiled at her just a little, for he had nearly forgotten how, and answered, "My heart has already been destroyed. You can do no more to harm it. Do not seek to know me, my lady. For me, there is no hope."

At that her lips curved into an answering smile, and Varich saw beyond her pretty words. He viewed her sharp teeth and the shrewd heat in her eyes. Her weird beauty lifted the darkness from his mind and, while he found himself caught, he realized what stood in his path: One of the dreaded Fomorians looked down at him with wide, unpitying eyes.

Now he knew what he had done. His despair had opened a doorway from the lady's prison in the Dreaming. His eyes narrowed as he studied her. Marena hissed and called forth her dark Glamour. As Fell closed in from all sides and the dark chimera from his own nightmares surrounded him, Varich reached for his sword, calling it to his hand. Hard and long he struggled, his sword slicing a bright path through the creatures on all sides. Sharp teeth tore at his legs as poisons fouled his blood. His magics failed him, and as his sight grew dim, he saw Marena smile. Icy darkness filled Varich, and he felt his heart reaching to meet it, yearning to end his pain.

Suddenly a brilliant gleam breached the darkness. Varich felt the warmth of the sun in his hand. The tangled weaving of his lost snow maiden's golden hair was glowing. With the last of his strength Varich threw his net upon the evil sorceress. The patterns wove around her, tying her hands, tangling in her hair and burning her with the purity of Varich's passion. Marena writhed in pain as she disappeared into the prison that was now her sanctuary, taking the golden net with her, for it burned its pattern onto her skin. As Varich lay dying, his parents came to him and poured living water into him to take the poisons from him. He told them of Marena, she whom they called Winter. He told them of his battle and the horrors he had faced. They brought him forth from the Dreaming to the high hills where the Vila dwell. There they spoke with their brothers and sisters, asking for recognition for the valor of their son. And thus it was that House Varich came to be, born from the deeds and the courage of its founder. Many flocked to Varich's banner, including those who valued bravery as well as those whose hearts could not be healed.

The Sundering

Many worshiped us as gods in our homeland, the great city of Novgorod. They made sacrifices to us of handsome serfs, carvings, enameled jewelry and fine pieces of amber worked in gold. We loved our Dreamers, treating them as vassals and children, as was only proper, making sure that they both loved us and feared us as well. Mortals danced on hillsides, spilling blood and flowers for our amusement in the days before the Shattering. After the Fomorians' betrayal, we mourned the changes to Varich. His heart grew dark and he vowed never to love another. Despite his sorrow, he ruled fairly and found his passions in war and politics.

We reveled in our land of endless forests, honoring the change of seasons as ice castles formed on the steppes to shield us in winter and silver birches bloomed lacy leaves to roof our summer circles. We ruled as golden threads shaping the tapestry of this world. Our subjects—the spirits of house, tree and field made flesh and the commoners whom we had chosen to affiliate with our grand and just house—were meant for our rule. Our Dreamers heard our music, gave us sacrifices, called us their gods! Amusing, yes, but not far from the truth in our minds.

Yet, in the heart of our realm the mortals who had dreamed for us alone began to have new dreams. Pale men in rough, dirty robes came from far away, twisting the dreams of our people, trading visions of the Varich and our servants for those of richly decorated beings they called saints, whose images they painted upon dead wood. "Christianity" came. At first, we thought to use it for our own ends. The passions of our people might be turned, for we too could appear as magic beings to do miracles for the masses. This was a mistake, for the worshipers of the bloody wooden sacrifice were jealous of our powers and our people's worship. They took our names and twisted them into the names of their holy men, trying to consume us as they ate the bread-flesh of their god. Legends and miracles were not enough. We watched as others struggled. Those loyal to us were tormented in fire and water and thrown to the wolves in the dead of winter. Hundreds of our Dreamers were slaughtered, and still we watched—for there would always be more, always had been more.

Some of us fought. Varich himself worked magics to shelter those who were loyal to us, beginning patterns that our Dreamers would follow through centuries of despair. Soothsayers, peering at flames through globes of amber, saw trods crumbling and fading as golden-roofed churches were built. The faces of our Dreamers turned from us in anger and fear. Screaming mobs of filthy animals that had once served us extinguished our Balefires that once had glowed as the sun on high hilltops.

There were more than enough reasons for leaving, and leave many of us did. Quietly we gathered our commoner servants, those favored Dreamers we had saved and the gifts that still pleased us. Panicking Seelie sidhe saw their first signs of trouble and chose to usurp power in this world to prevent the change. We gracefully gave in, allowing the Seelie to weave many of the threads that would lead to their downfall. The ever-changing worlds grew stagnant, bringing an end to the cycle of seasonal rule. Power in Arcadia would be ours, we who first saw the patterns and best prepared for the Great Winter. Varich gathered us together quietly. Before the other houses knew the Shattering was upon them, we left the mortal world, closing many of our trods behind us.

Departure and the Shattering

A few of our house stayed. Whether foolish or too fond of their earthbound dreams, a faction called the Obtenyani fought to keep our holdings and to stop Banality's onslaught. The leader of the Obtenyani, Wila Irynochka, saw the patterns ahead differently. Wily and rash young *rytsar* (knight) that she was, she gathered together those Dreamers whom Varich had saved from persecution and placed a Geas on them to remember us always and to hold to their dreams in secret and darkness until our return. Then, as trods shimmered and failed, as shortsighted houses came clawing in desperation at the gates, she fled with the last of our people, leaving behind our final Balefire, now no more than a faintly glowing cinder.

Arcadia: A World Carved of Ice

For centuries Arcadia, our beautiful homeland, has existed in the endless throes of unchanging winter. Although the flesh we must wear has fouled the memories of our days in Arcadia, we remember visions that came to us of patterns laid time and time again as we waited for some sign of spring's return. We looked in vain for revolution to follow stagnation so that Arcadia would open to new Glamour. Then the sign appeared: a red star gleaming in Arcadia's sky. The new crimson light stained snowy hills and towers of ice with the flush of a bloody abattoir. War, bloodshed, *change* was coming. The great circle of time finally signaled revolution. The Fomorians, enemies of the Vila, foes of most of the sidhe, have given us warning in the shape of a red orb—Balor's Eye—glowing in the midnight sky.

The Interregnum

What has happened in this world since we left? We know but little. Visions of this world were cut off from our sight during the centuries we dwelled in Arcadia. To us it seemed as though we left but a small time ago, yet the world has changed beyond recognition. What sorts of warriors live in this modern world? What dreams do Dreamers make? We must unravel the secrets of this new world quickly. From all we have heard, many of the commoners rebelled against their sidhe masters. We will not make the same mistakes as the houses that arrived before us. Our servants will once again answer our call to service. We have little time before the pattern completes itself. When it does, we will reign as masters of Winter here in the mortal world. Soon the Fomorians will arrive. We must be ready.

The Return

House Varich embodies the blood and bones of Mother Russia. We are the Dreams of the first people of that ancient land: the Avar, the Tatar and the Kazar. We are the vision of warriors who ride their stallions for days across the icy steppes to reach their enemies and slaughter without mercy. We are pictures in the mind's eye of craftsmen delicately applying rainbows of enamel and gold. We rule the spirits of the bathhouse, the forests and the air. We bid them, mortal and spirit, to remember us

through centuries of Seelie rule. Russia has changed. The voices of the *leshii*, the dryad and the spirits of the wind no longer sing in every breeze. Our homeland has many mortals, but Dreamers seem few. Many of those who still exist live in dark hopelessness, lost to Banality. Nevertheless, old patterns have reemerged. Dreamer shamans dance and sing broken fragments of their old paeans to us. Flames awaken on the hilltops where our Balefires once brightened the sky. Old pathways now lie open and vulnerable.

House Varich has returned. Yet some of us have found ourselves in lands only rumored to have existed when we left. New pathways have opened to a land called America. In that place, we find ourselves amid towers of stone that cover the sky, on a small piece of forested land called Central Park. Snow lies on the ground, but trees have buds pushing open against the ice. We will find our Dreamers here. Still others of our house have emerged in an alien place where the sea washes against a giant's toy bridge spun from webs of steel. High on a hill, along a curving road lined with colorful houses, we hear the voices of our people. They call this place Russian Hill, signifying that someone has already claimed it for us. This is very good. Our Dreamers remember.

Society: The Patterns of House Varich

Great passions once ruled the founder of our house. Varich's betrayal in love, however, has shaped our house and all its members. Though many of us still reflect Varich's fiery nature, yearning for impetuous action and longing to heed the calls to everlasting love, our vows constrain us. We live within the threads that Fate has woven for us, studying the patterns that rule our lives. Intricacies are dear to us, for they echo the webs that bind and shape us to our destiny. Rhythms amuse us, fix our attention and provide great joy as we decipher them. Dances, battle formations and the movements of fine equestrian performances all hold the same fascination. The strategy of combat and the interwoven strands of war, love, music and politics sustain us, icy substitutes for the vows of love lost to us.

House Blazon

House Varich's blazon is the sun ore on a field of sable, a golden sun on a black field. This symbol embodies the house colors of ebony and gold.

House Boon and Ban

Pattern-sense: Members of House Varich understand patterns. Given three rounds to watch a series of actions performed by another, such as sword fighting, dancing or sport, their difficulty in opposition or as a partner is lowered by 2 points. They may observe an opponent's patterns even while engaged in combat, they cannot fight one foe while observing a different one. Given a chance to observe three different times, they receive an extra die in addition to the decreased difficulty for that scene.

Loveless: House Varich sidhe can never give a vow of love to another. The other houses that came forth with them during the last few months know this flaw.

Challenge-Bound: They must accept all challenges. If a member of House Varich fails to acknowledge a challenge, she loses 1 point of Willpower per day until she returns the challenge. (Willpower lost in this fashion may not be recovered through the expenditure of experience points or by any other means until the character honors her challenge.) If a challenged member of the House is imprisoned to keep her from accepting the challenge, she loses 1 point of Strength for each day of her captivity (to a minimum of 1 point). If she remains imprisoned, her Stamina declines by 1 point per week until she "dies" (i.e., forgets her fae nature). As one might expect, house members take care to be courteous to each other and to stay in fighting trim.

Appearance

Most Varich sidhe have deep golden hair and dark eyes. A few are born with blue eyes, while some have sable hair that turns silver at the onset of their wilder years. Almost all Varich have high cheekbones and slanted eyes as well as very long, thick hair, often worn in braids. They tend to dress in brilliant scarlet or black voile, trimmed in fur and decorated with intricate patterns of gold cording. They especially love amber. Many of their treasures are either carved from amber or have amber decorations.

Organization

Much like the feudal society from which we arose, House Varich believes in the natural order of members' roles in their freeholds. Some may attempt to see the possibility of worthy individuals rising above their station, but few of us truly believe that "all men are created equal," no matter how often we hear quotes from the *Declaration of Independence* or the *Communist Manifesto*. Our servants, commoners and Inanimae alike, shall always serve. They may rise to the top of their rank, but without some great deed, they may go no further. The word of the head of a freehold is law. No one may gainsay a household's lord within his own holdings—not count, duke, nor even the High King himself.

Armies

As one might guess, the armies of House Varich consist of organized ranks of *rytsar* who command squads of foot soldiers. Mounted on tall, elegant horses, the *rytsar* serve as more than leaders. They also observe the ebb and flow of each battle, studying the movements of the enemy to exploit any of their flaws. Warriors of our house usually perform several feints to discern the enemy's patterns before making an all-out attack. Several ranking officers find places from which to observe the battle from every side, ready to follow our initial assault with reinforcements when the enemies' patterns become clear. Though this ability to discern patterns gives us a distinct advantage, it also serves as a potential weakness. If an enemy knows our tendency to take the time to determine their patterns, they may use that knowledge to deny us the opportunity to observe them, pressing their attacks before we can predict their movements.

Threads in Our Weaving

Do not think that we all adhere to the same beliefs just because we belong to one house. We, too, have our dissenters and our secret warriors.

Our house prospers because we do not cast out those who disagree with us.

Neither do we turn our backs on those who do our dirty work. We grow stronger because of these distinctive elements in our house.

The Obtenyani: The Changed Ones

From our house's beginning, some of us have followed a different pattern. Most eventually discover their foolishness in turning away from traditions and find their way back to our way of thinking. The Obtenyani, however, represent a faction that has not given up their deviations. No matter what the situation, the Obtenyani oppose our decisions, choosing to follow their heart instead of making rational decisions based on the patterns other members of our house have studied. Though the faction is comprised mostly of young sidhe and a few allied commoners, some individuals have belonged to the Obtenyani since the Sundering and cannot blame their current rebellions on youth. We tolerate our dis-

Oaths of House Varich

Oath of Adoption

One pattern I started, now I end it to begin anew in the name of Varich, founder of the house I take as my own. May my words be heard as truth and lived as truth and my actions follow the truth within my words forever in the name of my new house. May I never let a challenge go unanswered. May I never give a vow of true love to another. In the name of our father, the moon, and our mother, the sun, may I give honor to house Varich, adopted house, and serve it with my mind, my heart and my faith. If I foreswear my oath, may the sun and moon look upon me with disfavor, may all hands of my adopted house rise against me and may the pattern of my beating heart fall to stillness forever.

Changelings wishing to ally themselves with house Varich swear this oath in the presence of members of the Varich freehold willing to adopt them. The swearer recites the pledge twice—once at noon, when the sun reaches its zenith, and once at night, under the light of the moon. Because both sun and moon must witness this oath, no one may administer the oath of adoption on overcast days or during nights when there is no moon.

Challenge

Let no challenge go unanswered, for the courage of our house must be tested. The strength of our house must be measured. The honor of our house must never be in doubt. We shall prevail over any that might challenge us. Our will is strong, our courage mighty, our honor unequaled. So shall it be shown in tests against us.

All house members know this oath, for its speaking is required whenever a house member accepts a formal challenge. The speaking of the oath signifies acceptance and commits the swearer to engage in whatever form of combat or competition proposed to her. Varich fae who omit the oath suffer penalty of -1 to their dice pool for deciding the outcome of the challenge.

Vengeance

May the sun darken, may the moon turn black and may the call of the dreaming go unanswered if our vengeance be denied to us.

Though this oath has few words, its consequences belie its brevity. House members who take this oath of vengeance link themselves irrevocably to the necessity of carrying out their revenge. If a house member does not show some tangible progress toward fulfilling the oath, she may not gain glamour from any source, including the use of dross. Trods will not allow her passage in either direction (so it is not wise to swear this oath while in the near dreaming). The strictures of this oath end when the house member achieves her vengeance or dies in the attempt.

senters, however, because they represent the unexpected variations in the pattern and help us account for all options, even the most radical ones. Their leader, Wila Irynochka, is a *rytsar* who has distinguished herself in battle many times while searching the Dreaming for lost members of our house. Some say she seeks in particular for Varich's heart, lost to him in his dark wanderings.

The Nochnytza: Eclipse of the Sun

This secret order consists entirely of selected female members of the house. The Nochnytza makes no distinction between commoner and noble, but chooses members solely on the merits of their ability and loyalty to the house and to their elite society. The Nochnytza serves as a training ground for assassins dedicated to the survival of House Varich. Since no member of our house may refuse a challenge, many of our nobles might have died except for the work of these dedicated women, who use their deadly skills to eliminate potential threats before they become real ones.

The Nochnytza traces its origin to a time just before the Sundering, when many Varich lords fought losing battles against the incursion of Christianity. At the same time, warriors of our house struggled against Seelie sidhe who refused to listen to our warnings of impending disaster. Nochnytza do not always kill; sometimes intimidation or more subtle threats serve to dissuade those who would endanger house members. Many Nochnytza have mastered the patterns of hand-to-hand fighting in addition to the saber and whip. Opponents without honor fall prey to mysterious, lingering ailments, as some of the group have learned the ways of herbs. The leader of the Nochnytza changes once a year, at the time of the winter solstice. The current leader, a wilder rebel named Aleyeva, has broached the idea of extending the group's service to other worthy houses.

The Escheat

The Escheat details the traditional privileges and rights accorded to any noble and, in some instances, to commoners. We believe in the precise observation of these for both Unseelie and Seelie. However, it is amazing how the wording of the Escheat changes, depending upon the house.

The Right of Demesne

This gives a noble house the right to freeholds accorded to them by title and birth. It also points to the inalienable fact that a noble's freehold is his to rule as he wishes; no one may gainsay his word within his holding. To us, this portion of the Escheat needs no repeating. If it does, the holder has not applied his whip correctly or often enough.

The Right to Dream

The right to dream? Say, rather, the *duty* to dream. Our Dreamers *belong* to us; we muse them, shelter them and drive them to create works of beauty and wonder. In exchange, we gain Glamour. This is the way things have always been. We do not take the Dreamers of others unless we wish to call war against them. And we certainly would never deny another house their Dreamers unless that house neglects them so that they need our protection and patronage. We gladly give our protection to those who ask.

The Right of Guesting

House Varich generously follows the duty of guesting. Anyone who asks for shelter in our holdings receives food, a place by the stove and all the favors due a friend or ally. For those we trust, giving our hospitality is an honor. For those we do not know, it is a way to learn more of a stranger's motivations and methods. For our enemies, it is a necessity. We understand that it is better to have a foe in your home than in the shadows behind it.

Our house has a reputation for lavish festivals and gatherings with many competitions. No one leaves our tables unsatisfied; we do not allow it. Balalaikas ring as we dance until we have no more energy to move. When that happens, our satyrs come and we dance again, this time with heated blood, body against body. Anyone may join in the dances, although we exact severe penalties for serious missteps. We *are* pattern and do not lightly endure those who cannot follow one. It is a pleasure and a danger to be a non-Varich guest among us. You will soon learn the exhilaration of existence on the edge of pain.

The Right of Ignorance

The Seelie now believe that we must stay hidden? No wonder fewer Dreamers exist! How can mortals dream for us if we skulk in the shadows like cowardly sluagh? We will not become whispering ghosts to satisfy those too timid to live. Perhaps we need to hide ourselves from mortal eyes for the moment, but as Winter returns and the Fomorians send their monsters to destroy all who oppose them, we will emerge from hiding and proclaim our existence openly. We must have strength from Dreamers and mortals who *know* we exist. It will be interesting to see their reactions as well as the expressions on the faces of the Seelie cowards who have faded to nothing because of their timidity. Believe that this time we will hold our Dreamers safe while gathering even more as servants, soldiers and playthings. We now understand that, at least in this, the Obtenyani were correct: We need Dreamers. In this age still subjugated by its dead wooden god, these Dreamers must be nurtured and preserved.

The Right of Life

For House Varich the right of life is very important. We do not kill other sidhe. Torture, perhaps; change their minds, yes; but *kill?* No. That would be too brutish and unkind. Never let it be said that we are anything but courteous to our cousins, both Seelie and Unseelie. One caveat, however. We meet any challenges fully with the courage and determination of our house. If someone happens to die in such a challenge, the fault belongs to the one who so foolishly sought death at our hands.

The Right of Rescue

Rescuing those who have been lost to Banality or who languish in the captivity of unbelievers is a joy to us. We find it interesting to see the patterns that lead to such a loss and the weavings we must create to rescue those in need. If we save enemies from the clutches of those who would destroy their fae souls, we gain allies who will fight on our side, perhaps even against their own allies.

Allies and Enemies

Now that we have returned, we must establish once again our ties with those houses that once served as our allies and make certain that the houses that once opposed us do not offer us a significant threat. Both nobles and commoners have gone through many changes since we last walked these lands. We cannot afford to underestimate anyone.

The Nobles: Rulers by Birth

Some of the noble houses have already staked their claim on the mortal world. Though they have ruled for three decades unopposed, we have returned to offer challenge to them. We represent the interests of those who see the necessity of patterns and of the alternation of Seelie and Unseelie influences. We hope to find allies among those who returned with us and, perhaps, even among some of the other houses, though they may not welcome us at first.

House Aesin

The Unseelie members of this house follow their own code of honor. We salute them for their independence. They have, however, the subtlety of a Viking warship in full sail. They see only the doom-filled final conflict ahead, much as the ignorant Norsemen who influenced them. Too bad they cannot see beyond the end of their world. Perhaps it is for the best. We shall keep them as allies and allow them to enter Valhalla in the service of our house when the Fomorians come. Aesin will serve as a good front line. We will look beyond the battle and pick up the pieces. Perhaps they will find the Ragnarök they seek.

House Ailil

The members of this house breathe political acumen and subtlety. They understand the turning of the seasons and manipulate patterns nearly as well as we. We shall do all we can to make sure the Silver Dragon fights on the side of the Sun when war begins, for they also understand the futility of denying either side of our nature. Until then we will watch and learn. The Ailil have had more time in this world to create a network of spies, and we can benefit from their knowledge if we can convince them to make common cause with us. Dragons are wily creatures and very likely to surprise those who do not watch them. We do not make that mistake; we know the Dragons' strengths and weaknesses too well for that.

House Balor

How to describe our feelings for this house? From the beginning we have known of their slyness and untrustworthiness, yet we find something very attractive about them. Wounded, constantly imperfect, they take pride in their faults and flaunt them as treasures. We suspect them of having more in common with our Fomorian enemies than with the Vila from which we came. If this is true, this house shall know the approach of Winter before any other house. Our duty shall lead us to stay close, no matter what the final cost to them—or us.

House Beaumayn

Many members of this French house believe they understand the patterns of the future better than we do. They prophesy doom and ending times. Despite the Mists, we retain memories of their tiresome storm-crow mouthings. They bring doom upon themselves by their words, as they did when they undertook their experiments with cold iron. Although we admired their courage, we approved the decision to imprison them for their rash actions. Be wary of them, for if they remember our part in their banishment, they may decide that vengeance carries more import than prophecy.

House Daireann

What can we say about those who care only for battle? Place them at the front of the fray and let them do what they do best. There is little complexity in the weavings of their minds or politics. That makes them easy to deal with.

House Dougal

This house of crafters and metalsmiths can be very useful in times of war. We will treat them with all the respect we treat our most talented servants if they are willing to forge well for us. They will know our enmity if they are not.

House Eiluned

Sorcerers and gossips, members of House Eiluned spend their existence searching for secrets and holding them close. In many ways they remind us of the cowardly sluagh in their love for secrecy and elusiveness. Still, they can be quite powerful, and they have familial connections to House Ailil, a house we have always considered an ally. If they did not choose to ally with the Seelie court, we could respect them for their mastery of the Arts. Perhaps someday they will realize their true affiliation or reveal to us the secret they have held for so long: that they are actually Unseelie as well.

House Fiona

We have long admired this courageous and passionate house. When most of our house left for Arcadia, House Fiona fought beside the Obtenyani until the Shattering drove everyone away from the mortal world. Though they're foolish in their passions, their bravery makes up for a great deal. We lament their lack of trust in us; it seems they feel that more from our house should have remained in the world until the last possible moment. Perhaps they have learned to control their passions since reentering the world.

House Gwydion

This house provides reason why we do not call ourselves Seelie. They do not understand the infinite variations in the patterns of the world and cannot see beyond their own narrow interpretations of honor and the Escheat. Too bad for them! They are good fighters and strong leaders—not as accomplished as our house in either, but capable all the same. We should consider calling a challenge or two on them to keep both our houses in good fighting shape before the true war begins.

House Leanhaun

Weak and nearly useless, the members of this house attempt to befriend everyone, making their friendship worth nothing. I have yet to see anything worthwhile about them except their ability to make friends. Rest assured, however, that members of this house will find it difficult to seduce us into alliances, no matter how amiably we may act toward them.

House Liam

This house tried to find Glamour among Christian believers and chose to side with the church that persecuted our Dreamers. We suspect, however, that they eventually found themselves barred from the religion they so fervently embraced. Perhaps they have learned a few lessons since their return, but we do not hold out great hopes for them.

House Scathach

Seekers of weakness in Fate's pattern, most of this house remained behind after the Shattering, priding themselves on mixing their blood with mortals. Somehow they believe that diluting their fae nature will bring them victory in the coming war. Always their eagerness to work outside the patterns of Fate shows their untrustworthiness. House Varich does not hate them, but many of us pity them. They do not truly understand the patterns they work to destroy. A few members of House Scathach, the wisest ones, left for Arcadia not long after we did. Now they have returned. We shall watch with interest the patterns of their reactions to their faithless, half-human cousins.

Commoners: Born to Serve

Commoners make useful servants. While the Inanimae provide most of the help we need in our freeholds, they are limited to certain places. Our peasants possess more versatility, though they also claim more independence than we might like. We treat our servants with respect, for we realize the importance of giving even the least of our household the honor they deserve. Still, we know that servants may turn against us—no sluagh is *ever* allowed within one of our freeholds without swearing the most powerful of oaths—and we realize the smallest mouse can kill a wolf, provided it has the advantage of position and circumstance. You would do well to remember how many patterns are shaped by commoners' actions.

Boggans

Gossips and homebodies, boggans serve as the connection between us and our house spirits. Boggans always remember to leave a bowl of milk on the doorstep and to save a bit of steam in our bathhouse each night. These helpful commoners get along with the lesser house and hearth spirits, complementing each other's skills. Woe to the freehold, however, where the relationship between domestic spirits and boggan caretakers succumbs to jealousy and envy.

Eshu

We remember these commoners from long ago. As graceful on horseback as the tribes of the steppes, the eshu often appeared among the nomads of our tundra and taiga. Always listen to their stories, for they see the patterns that connect freehold to freehold and duchy to duchy. Though they couch their facts in fable, they reveal important secrets. We honor all storytellers but reserve the best place by the hearth for the eshu. We believe they will be some of the first to see the signs of the coming Winter. We shall do all we can to ensure their friendship.

Nockers

How can we resist the impossible, complex toys created by these makers of intricacies? Through flattery and respect for this hardy group of commoner crafters, we hope to gain the weapons and armor necessary for the coming battle—and if they produce toys in the meantime, who are we to protest? The items they make entertain us.

Pooka

Which is true and which is a lie? The pooka twist their words so much it is an amusing puzzle to figure out what they mean to tell us. Do not dismiss them merely as liars and fools. Pooka have much to tell those who are willing to untangle their web of words. They are also very loyal when treated well, as are most good servants.

Redcaps

Uncouth, straightforward, unalterably obnoxious, redcaps are no better than pigs for eating refuse, yet they easily make the best frontline shock troops. Though we do not invite them to the head table, they are welcome to clean up the scraps after the feast. If they showed the least sign of complexity, we might find them interesting. For now, we will consider them expendable soldiers, whip them to the front line and keep them downwind of us and out of our bathhouses.

Satyrs

Ah, the satyrs: The dances they dance, the music they make! They are the most interesting of the commoners. We invite them to our celebrations, listen to their scholarly wisdom, appreciate and join in their wild abandon. No Varich freehold would be complete without at least one satyr as house lore keeper or mentor for our fosterlings.

Sluagh

Treacherous, slimy, cowardly traitors—what else is there to say? Since one of their kind betrayed our founder, we have considered the sluagh our enemy. They hoard secrets within their tiny, dark hearts, whispering lies with their toothless mouths. Their secrecy and duplicity obscure and destroy patterns. Sluagh are a canker in the heart of the Dreaming, pretending to live as Seelie to gain protection from us. We would spare a Fomorian before granting mercy to one of these soft, rotting creatures smelling of mouse droppings and dust. Do you know how hard it is to make a sluagh scream? I do. But it is worth the effort.

Trolls

To those of House Varich, trolls are known as *volos*. Renowned for keeping sacred oaths, they are some of the few commoners we trust implicitly. As different from sluagh as they can possibly be, *volos* will give themselves to you for life and beyond so long as you can win their loyalty. Although we are Unseelie, we seek the loyalty of trolls from both Summer and Winter Courts. The first make uncomplicated shields and loyal servants; the second are harder to draw to your service but prove more willing and flexible in times of war.

Lost Ones

We have heard that some members of our house have become creatures known as Lost Ones, nobles who refused to leave the mortal world when the Shattering occurred but chose to surround themselves in pockets of Glamour rather than take on human shells. Now these Lost Ones dwell in hidden places, cut off from both the mortal world and the Dreaming. Since our return, some of the Obtenyani, under the leadership of Wila Irynochka, have taken it upon themselves to search for these secret realms in the hope of rescuing those who have been trapped in their own dreams for centuries.

Thallain

Though now a shadow rises to occlude what we knew while in Arcadia, we remember Thallain and their terrible guises. While hordes of beasties and boggarts, goblins and ogres fell, the Thallain still surrounded our castles and tore at the walls. Hunting them was dangerous; not hunting them was suicidal. Some fae think they can use these monstrosities. We, however, recognize that their patterns are too simple for anything other than killing or dying. Along with the Fell, they serve the Fomorians and await their masters' call. Destroy them when you can, send them to your enemies when you cannot. They call themselves Unseelie; we call them insane.

A Rus by Any Other Name: Varich Terms for the Inanimae

Here is a list of most of the Inanimae as they are known to the members of House Varich.

Domestic Spirits

Spirits of the hearth and home are as powerful and helpful as the size and magnificence of their Anchors, as well as the amount of respect paid to them, allows them to be. No Varich holding is complete without them, and no member of House Varich will knowingly insult these helpful spirits.

Bannik: The spirit of the bathhouse, the *bannik* is often malicious if not treated with deference and given the last bath of the evening. *Banniks* help those they favor by giving them visions in the waters these spirits control.

Domovoi: A powerful spirit of dwellings, the *domovoi* often takes on the visage of a respected person of the family to speak to those whose home he guards. He knows most of the secrets of his freehold. Unless given proper and constant respect, a *domovoi* may divulge these secrets to enemies.

Dvorovoi: An animal spirit of the yard, the *dvorovoi* can be very mischievous to those who do not feed or treat him well. *Dvorovoi* often take the shape of cats to wander and explore their territory.

Kikimora: The most helpful spirit of the household, the *kikimora* does chores such as weaving and other domestic tasks. Anyone who sees her work should be certain to admire her talents or may find burnt bread, clothing tied in knots or flasks filled with vinegar in retaliation.

Polevik: Lush and voluptuous, these field nymphs, both male and female, find fascination in the various fertility rites practiced by those who understand the connection between sex and plowing fertile ground.

Wild Spirits

The wild spirits of Russia have suffered from the poisons poured into the water, land and air. Some of them, particularly those with Anchors in the Dreaming, have managed to keep themselves nearly unchanged throughout the centuries since the Shattering. The Varich do not pay as much attention to them as they do the Inanimae servants sharing their freeholds, but they do understand their power.

Berenginy: Beautiful nymphs with flowing, dark hair, these lovely spirits sing to draw lovers to them but sometimes do not wish to let them go. They dwell along riverbanks and will pull their admirers down to stay with them forever in the murky water along the shore. Many *russalki* have been created this way. If it were not for their wisdom and their ability to know most of what happens along the river they serve, the dangers of consulting them would outweigh any benefit.

Leshii: Horned spirits of the forest, the *leshii* look like a combination of an old tree covered with moss and an antlered man. They refer to their leader as the "Lord of the Forest." He awakened during the Resurgence and works to influence any that might stop the destruction of the lands he has sworn to protect.

Vodyanoi: These mercurial Inanimae of lakes and ponds are friendly to those who use the Anchors they protect as long as they receive gifts and respect. Trouble follows those ignorant of the need for proper thanks and an occasional splash of vodka in the water. The *vodyanoi* overturn boats of those who do not treat them properly. Anyone who deliberately snubs them should remember to stay off the water if he wishes to survive, for the *vodyanoi* call lightning down on those they dislike.

Gallain

The Gallain, at least those who dwell close to the natural world, once served us well. We have heard, however, that these creatures also have changed in the centuries since our departure. The new patterns they weave may be important to us.

Fomorians

We do not know whether Fomorians walk upon this world now, although all patterns point to their imminent arrival. We have heard of creatures called fomori, who may be lesser children of our great foe, though far cruder and more Banal than true Fomorians. Perhaps we

will fight them as practice for the coming wars.

Inanimae: Spirits of the Rus

Our hills and homes remember us and will learn to do us homage in the dance of servant to master yet again.

—Sergei Malaruski, Grump noble of House Varich, upon his arrival.

Abandoned, lost to the chill winds of banality, even in our repose our anger festered and burned. Do not expect the bannikitza to bow, nor our tainted waters to come lap against the feet of our so-called masters.

—Alma, rebel *bannik* bathhouse spirit, upon the coming of Sergei Malaruski to his old holdings.

The Inanimae, spirits of the earth and sky, have always been our servants, our children. Many have lost their way in the Russian darkness. Their voices haunt us. Few return to our fold. When House Varich ruled all the Russians, the land teemed with Inanimae. These spirits were part of everything for the fae—the earth, the rivers, their freeholds and the endless taiga surrounding them. We understood how to please these spirits as well as how to use them.

Many of the Inanimae served as household servants, gardeners and keepers of their forestlands. Some acted as guides within the Dreaming. Others stayed near the homes of Dreamers to remind them of the magical world around them and to work for those House Varich wished to favor. In exchange the Inanimae received honors and gifts for their loyal service. The Kithain protected their Anchors.

When House Varich left, some Inanimae who had Anchors in the Dreaming came with them to Arcadia. However, many Inanimae were left to the mercy of the post-Shattering world and either fell into Somnolence or had their Anchors destroyed as pagan sites of worship. With the Resurgence of three decades ago, the sleeping land awoke to its spirits.

Unfortunately, many of the surviving Inanimae of Russia suffer from the pollution in the land, water and sky. Those who returned with House Varich are very loyal to them and will not expect the terrible reception they receive from their brothers and sisters in the Autumn World

Prodigals

Whether or not these mysterious creatures were once children of the Dreaming, their lives now possess a very different pattern from those of the fae. We know very little about them, though sometimes we have faint memories of our relations with them before the Shattering. What role, if any, they play in our future we have yet to determine.

Upyri

Although some of us believe the *upyri*, or vampires, once stood among the ranks of the fae, others of us feel that what the peasants believe may be closer to the truth: that they are corpses inhabited by the unclean spirits of evil sorcerers. For centuries the witch Baba Yaga, rumored to be one of the *upyri*, sent nightmares into the Dreaming. Now we rejoice to hear that she has disappeared. We have heard of others, however, who gather mortals for twisted sorcerous experiments. Do not let the *upyri* near you unless you carry a long stake of ash wood and a very sharp, real sword.

Werewolves

Long ago, we met some of the changing wolf peoples. The first of their kind sprang howling from our forests of pine and silver birch to become their nobility. Many of the wolf-kind work with the *leshii* to preserve our lands. Some of the wolf folk even attended our celebrations to dance in honor of the changing seasons. Other wolf folk, known for their bloody claws, possess more savagery and cause our Dreamers to fear the Moon, our father. Winter hunts in pursuit of these killers has always been a favored though dangerous sport of ours.

Ghosts

Many sad spirits wander in the darkness of our rivers, roam through the dank mists in our forests or scream in agony in the pits beneath our feet in the mossy taiga. We know them. *Russalka* call to us, water dripping from their limbs as they beg for our help. Some of them are Dreamers lost to us in the purges of the followers of the crucified god. Others ghosts are new to us, but they wail with the same voices, with the same accusations, telling us of murders and purges during the long centuries of our absence. We can do little for them except seek vengeance for their murders. In time, we tell them, in time.

Sorcerers

Many mortals have tried to gain the power of the fae. Few have the blood of the kinain that may allow them to access Glamour and the world of the Dreaming. Some of us remember tainted sorcerers fighting wars over access to power. Others followed their tortured god and chanted songs of joy over the crackling fires and screams from our kinsmen. All should be approached with caution.

Mortals

Upon our return, we have noticed with great perplexity how other sidhe treat mortals. What is the point of watching humans from afar and yearning for their Glamour when it is all there for the taking? If humans created us from their dreams, they dreamed us as their masters. In the past we did not take part in most mortal doings, for they did not interest us. Why spend time in the bower with the cattle? We showered our favor only on mortals who were truly passionate and artistically skilled. Still, we had many favorites and often enchanted artisans to decorate our freeholds and create adornments for us. We needed no servants, for the house spirits worked for us industriously and without complaint. Now we have learned our lesson. We will watch mortals, see how others influence them and work to bring back the worship we have lost. We will have mortal servants, human lovers, Dreamers as playthings. They will teach us what we must know to claim this world as our own.

Our Rod: The Kinain of House Varich

Although in the past we did not think of mortals as equal to us, we had no problem with joining them in celebrations or taking them as lovers when the mood struck. Better to love someone who will not be hurt by your refusal to join with her in oaths of fidelity than to cause anger or mistrust among our own. A few possess the spark of Glamour, particularly those who kept their belief in us throughout the centuries. We shall first gather these as our servants and advisers in this modern world. So far we have found branches of our kinain in many places?among shamans in Siberia, with "black marketeers" (whatever that term might mean) in Novgorod and among a group of pagan Lithuanian bards. Others dwell in the new lands far to the west, and we shall work quickly to discover them and claim them for our own.

Treasures of House Varich

Our house has a weakness for certain items. Creations of amber and gold, devices made or decorated with a complex pattern and luxurious furs, finely wrought swords and unusual magical toys all appeal to us. Those wishing our favor soon learn what gifts to bring us. The items detailed below are special to our house and have been given to heroes at various times in our history.

The Amber Wyrm

Rare Treasure, Level 3

Deep within a dark red amber egg lies a miniature dragon coiled in sleep. Suspended on a golden chain, surrounded by a patterned web of gold, the egg is translucent, allowing all details of the dragon to be seen. On occasion the dragon turns in its slumber, as though the amber were merely water.

If this Treasure is taken within the Dreaming, the user may spend 1 point of Glamour and call forth a chimerical dragon (with 1 point of Glamour). The dragon will fight as a Level 5 chimera for its caller if granted a suitable gift of gold or amber. The creature fights until destroyed or called back to its egg. This may be done once a month.

The Eyes of the Snow Maiden

Singular Treasure, Level 4

In ancient times, the sorceress Charodei used pieces of golden amber, clear as sunshine, to make the eyes of the ice maiden she presented to our founder, Varich. When Varich's passion destroyed her, the amber eyes were discovered submerged in a pool of strangely salty water. Varich never wished to see them again, but other members of the house have kept them, for it is rumored that they may truly see the shapes of our enemies, the Fomorians.

If an individual holds the amber pieces up to her own eyes and looks through them, she can see as if she possessed Kenning 5 for purposes of discerning the presence of creatures related to the Dreaming. She may also see through illusions and other forms of magical disguise.

Firebird

Rare Treasure, Level 4

This nocker-built Treasure is an intricate mechanical firebird made of ruby and gold. When exposed to both the light of the sun and the rays of the moon, the firebird soars and sings into the sky when commanded to do so. When it has risen to a height of 100 feet, it bursts into glorious flame, lighting the area around it for miles with a golden, flickering light and pointing the way to the nearest trod or to a specific location designated by its master. The explosion does not harm the firebird, which stays high overhead until called back or until the next sunrise, at which point it returns to its golden perch and slumbers until called forth again. The firebird may point the way to only one place with each awakening.

The Famous and the Infamous

Although we have yet to make our mark in the modern world, we bring with us unique and vibrant individuals whose actions should soon command the attention they deserve. We consider ourselves fortunate that those who lead us do so with an awareness of both our past and our future.

Varich, Child of the Sun and Moon

The son of Miesiac (the Moon) and Dazbóga (the Sun), both members of the legendary Vila, Varich possesses dark golden hair like his mother and slanted, heavy-lidded eyes as black as the night ruled over by his father. A rash youth born of contrasts and contrariness, Varich displays his mother's fiery heat in battle yet reflects his father's cool intellect in all things magical. Unfortunately, in the process of trying to find a worthy mate for their perfect son, his eager parents damaged Varich's heart beyond repair, rendering him incapable of ever giving his love to another.

Varich has ruled his house for many centuries with an even hand and a just temperament, although he has never lost the darkness and pain he felt. He remembers everything and still yearns for his impossible love. He knows well who betrayed him and does not allow his hatred to cool with the centuries. For him, it was only yesterday, and the time spent in Arcadia did nothing to calm him.

Upon his return to the mortal world, he chose to take the body of a dancer in a professional theater group—an inspired choice, since he now gains Glamour from the patterns he helps to create on stage. He owns a fine Queen Anne–style mansion overlooking the bay in San Francisco. His greatest wish is to understand and conquer the patterns of the Endless Winter so that he may drive the Fomorians away when they arrive. Still, he fears what he sees in the pattern of the future.

Rytsar Wila Irynochka

This wilder sidhe knight started the order called Obtenyani, or the Changed Ones, because she felt Varich's plans to leave the world early were rash and unfair to the house's Dreamers and the Inanimae who could not leave their Anchors. She and her band of house rebels stayed to fight beside the Seelie houses, succeeding in preserving some of our Dreamers and convincing them to remember House Varich during the centuries we remained in Arcadia. Opinionated and rash at times, Irynochka is a silver-haired beauty with slanted, dark eyes. She has survived many challenges through her intelligent choice of weapons, and she acts as the "worthy opposition" in an advisory capacity to Varich. Her human host belonged to a member of a band in the Castro district. She has since learned to play the drums and has continued as the percussionist for the Sirens, a lesbian rock band.

House Scathach: Restless Shadows

Tiger Trap

Normandy, June 1944, under starry skies, Standartenführer Hans Heydrich stood tall in the cupola of his black King Tiger tank. Unlike many of his comrades in the Waffen SS, inhuman men who sought to conceal their atrocities behind a veneer of Teutonic duty and respectability, the sable-clad redcap colonel proudly displayed his crimes for all those with eyes to see. In the dream-lit halo of Kenning, the liquidation of the Warsaw Ghetto and the shadows of the Oradour-sur-Glane massacre glistened around him like crimson cobwebs. Garlands of skulls festooned his pet tiger, and its treads, sticky with blackened blood, tore deep claw marks in the idyllic French country lane.

Heydrich smiled as he passed the ramshackle contours of a gutted school building. He rarely gave it a second thought these days, but he had been a small-town schoolmaster himself before the war—a nobody. Over fifteen years ago, however, the black dreams of National Socialism had rekindled his true nature. Exposing twin rows of razor sharp teeth, the colonel gave a wolf's smile to Lieutenant Bock, who rode nearby in an accompanying half-track. Hungry red eyes gleamed coldly in the moonlight as the two redcaps silently communed over the feast of carnage they would soon bring to the unsuspecting hamlet below.

The days of wine and roses were over for the proud Nazi conquerors who had swept so gloriously into Paris only four years before. Those had been heady days, when the Third Reich had spread out its hand and swept aside its enemies in brutal, wheeling arcs. Now the Black Angel of Oradour-sur-Glane road forth, not on a grand mission of conquest, but on a little matter of bookkeeping. The corrupt Vichy regime was fast crumbling, and with its dissolution came increased activity by the French Resistance. The Maquis had blown an ammunition depot nearby, and intelligence had tracked their activities to the village below. Heydrich's reasons for requesting the assignment could be described in one word: Kithain.

That there was a changeling core to the resistance in this valley, the colonel had no doubt. Meddlesome boggans most likely, though he smelled the stench of trollish involvement behind it all somewhere. No matter. Among the 150 men in the column behind him were over a dozen fanatical young Dreamers from the Hitlerjugend. Even more important, there were six of his own corby, fellow redcaps with whom he had drunk deeply from the Dark Glamour of war. With these he would smash any fae-backed assault from the weakling French Maquisards. His outriders called in the all-clear signal and the Tiger rumbled down the thinly wooded road, its leisurely pace belying its mission of murder.

Hardened on the Eastern Front, Heydrich was prepared for any eventuality, but even his eyes betrayed surprise as his tank unexpectedly lurched to a halt around a bend in the road. A pale woman in French provincial garb stood in the shadows; raven hair framed a slender face filled with black reproach. Heydrich's eyes glinted with the second sight, laying bare the woman's true form. Her white peasant's dress melted away, revealing a coat of shimmering scales and a dark grey cloak. Around her neck hung a miniature hourglass, and she held a slender silver blade. She was obviously fae, but the colonel felt disturbed that he couldn't divine her lineage. Too tall and stately for a boggan and clearly not a troll—perhaps one of those interfering Spanish eshu?

"It is late, frauen," he smiled, giving a gentlemanly Junker bow. "Are you lost? It is a dangerous time for such a pretty young morsel to be wandering alone in the woods. The barbarian Allies are afoot and have no respect for a woman's virtue. Come with us and we will find you food and comfort."

"My thanks, but I come as servant, lord and messenger. The people of this valley are my obligation and do not desire you here. You may leave, little colonel, or die these two full months before your allotted time."

"Then you are Joan of Arc, come to rescue La Belle France from her tormenters? Stupid bitch! The days of knightly valor are long past, and your toy sword is no match for tanks or bullets." To kill another changeling with the weapons of Autumn went against the Escheat, but he had dared worse, and the Dreaming had yet to collect its debt.

The merest inclination of Heydrich's head and Bock's machine gun barked its war cry. The woods erupted with phosphorescent fireflies as the woman leapt skyward in a storm of splinters. The lieutenant was a master of weapons, both of dream and steel, and he was supernaturally fast. She, by contrast, seemed to move in slow motion, a

leaf buffeted by a gentle breeze. As she lighted on the vehicle's hood, however, the fast-moving redcap's face registered shock for the split second before her leather-jacketed foot crushed his throat.

Heydrich stood astride his turret now, his own black blade in one hand and his pistol in the other. A grenade tore a second half-track apart behind him, its burning engine painting the surrounding shadows a garish orange. More shots echoed throughout the column, their staccato shrill punctuated by war cries, both French and German, human and fae. The woman spun like a ballerina on the half-track's hood, but Heydrich had found her range. His luger flashed, and the woman's face creased in pain as the bullet tore through her shoulder, but the only sound that came from her was the shattering of glass as she smashed her ornamental hourglass. Heydrich grinned, but inside he felt fear. Why was she so silent? He aimed again; this shot would take the slut's head clean off.

Suddenly his pet Tiger roared to life once more, lunging forward but wildly out of control. Its treads left the narrow lane, lurching sickeningly and pitching the SS man from his perch, face first into a tree. Coughing bark, he turned just in time to see the tank's great grinding wheels come crashing down on him. Almost 69 tons of clanking steel sheered through his legs, severing them at the knees. Shrieking madly, he cleared the

juggernaut's treads as it lumbered blindly into the darkness. Heydrich spat blood and grasped his blade in his trembling hands. The woman stood above him now. Her eyes flashed black, twin mirrors reflecting nothing but death, terrible and sure.

"I, I know what you are now," he rasped between chattering, blood stained teeth. He had never thought much about the tales of the shining ones who had left some 600 years ago, but there was no doubt in his mind what it was that stood before him. "Why have you returned? Why now?"

"Returned? No, little schoolmaster, not returned. We have always been here." Her voice seemed almost kind, or perhaps it was pity? Heydrich feebly raised his sword to block her whirling silver blade, but it shattered in his hands. A flash of pain and his world turned to roaring red, then hissing black, then silence.

Two months later, the resistance found the cripple in an abandoned farmhouse. He wore civilian clothes and claimed to be a simple teacher—hungry, broken, lost. But there was soon little doubt that this was none other than the cursed Black Angel of Oradour-sur-Glane. The Maquis's justice in such matters ran swift and sure. His last words were of a dark woman who haunted his dreams, but, if she ever existed, she had returned to the restless shadows.

Prelude

Houses Gwydion, Fiona and Balor. Forgive my laughter; I am just gratified that three families as disparate as yours have put aside their enmity to capture a lowly "half-sidhe" such as myself. After all these centuries, it is good to see that House Scathach's ability to unite others remains undiminished. I admire your courage for daring the Winterweir to capture me, but less so your wisdom in interfering with a daughter of Scathach's missionæor in thinking you can hold her. But I see you are curious. What moves one of the Tuatha de Danaan's first children, even one with blood so debased as mine, to take up arms against her fellow nobles? We have a long journey before you can deliver me to face what passes for justice in Concordia these days. My house is not known for its conviviality, but neither are we mute. Ask your questions and I will answer.

Common Nobility

(The History of House Scathach, as told to Lady Victoria ap Gwydion)

Let us speak plainly, as befits our warrior houses. One of your companions sought me out to gain knowledge and aid for his beleaguered keep, the other for power. You, on the other hand, simply seek my death. Ah, Gwydion, ever so swift in judgment. So, you blame me for your brother's death during the Shattering. Fair enough. I plead guilty. You may remember him with sisterly affection, but the White Plains pooka who made their home near Silver's Gate have a different memory of him: as an oppressor and, ultimately, as a butcher.

I caught up with him in the Bullydales; in person he was something of a disappointment. I had expected a calculating monster and found instead a callow wilder, far better with his tongue than with a blade. "Stand aside, half-blood, and let your betters pass!" He had a skillful feint, but a less than impressive *prise de fer* and an abysmal parry. I sent him sprawling in the creek but would have granted him an honorable surrender if only he had not ordered his trolls against me. By so doing, he sealed his fate. Even among my own house, I am not known for my forbearance. Still, I will not dispute your right to revenge. We of House Scathach stand accused of far worse. . . .

The Second Battle of Moytura

Our tale begins with a creature known as the Morrigan. Her name means *Phantom Queen*, and she was a grand enigma, even to the other Tuatha de Danaan. Humanity worshipped her as a goddess of battle, ecstasy, fertility and magic. She was instrumental in securing the Tuatha de Danaan's victory over the fir-bholg in the First Battle of Moytura, and in the second—well, we shall see.

After the fir-bholgs' defeat, both the Tuatha de Danaan and the Fomorians observed an uneasy truce, but such a condition could not last long between two forces so diametrically opposed. In the last war, Nuada, then king of the Tuatha de Danaan, lost his hand and replaced it with one of silver. There were those among the Children of Dana who, foolishly, felt this handicap disqualified him from rulership. In his stead, they installed Bres the Beautiful—son of a Tuatha woman and a Fomorian king—upon the Falian Throne. It was not long, however, before the Tuatha de Danaan realized they had made a terrible mistake. With the Children of Dana increasingly arrayed against him, Bres sought out his father's brood to solidify his claims by force.

Shall we speak of names? Those who led the invading horde had names that still possess power, long after those who bore them have passed beyond. One among them was Balor, lord of the Fire Court. Another was Indech, scion of the then nascent Ivory Court and hunts marshal for King Tethra of the Emerald Dream. Just as important to our story is Indech's son, Octriallach. Not yet one of the potentates of the age, he was nevertheless clever and subtle, with a far-reaching eye for magic. With these and countless others, the Fomorian War Dream cloaked itself in a nightmare gale and swept out over tenebrous seas toward the isles of the sane.

Meanwhile, in the Tuatha de Danaan's quest for allies, the god Dagda returned to his fastness in Glenn Etin. There, a year before, he had made a love pact with the Morrigan and now sought her for her wisdom. Since that time she had borne his child, a girl she had named Scathach (meaning *the Shadowy One*) for her black hair and shadow-grey eyes. Upon their reunion, the Morrigan foretold many things, including the imminent end of the current age and the place where the Fomorians would first emerge from their nightmare trods.

I relate these tales as they are oft repeated in the Irish myths, but this was no battle for a mere island, no matter how fertile in dreams. This was a war that stretched throughout dimensions uncountable. Ireland was but one of many places where the battle leaked into the Autumn realms (I believe the Trojan Wars were another). Still, to simplify matters, I shall stick to the standard text.

The battle joined in earnest. The Tuatha's ally Lugh and Balor of the Piercing Eye met in single combat. The Red King opened his cyclopean eye, and a poisonous crimson light crept out across the plains, killing thousands before Lugh drove his spear through the Fomorian's brain. Balor was not the only Great One on the scene, however; the second monarch is of far more consequence to our story. In a narrow valley, Indech and the Morrigan came face to face. Inhumanly beautiful in visage but with the body of a great wyrm, the White King laughed when he saw the lone woman before him. He drew his blade, the Sword of Tethra, a fearsome sliver of stormy night with an emerald shimmering above the hilt.

"By this sword, forged in green fire, stand aside, woman. I am Indech Oneira-Osseus. Where I pass, nightmares slip loose of slumber's shackles and feast upon their Dreamers." But the Morrigan did not move.

"Then by the Fates who have promised that I will deliver destruction during the nights of Final Winter, I command you fall!" he thundered. Cracks appeared in the White King's beautiful visage as he gave himself up to his rage and swung his great sword toward the unarmed woman. Another potent blade parried it in a shower of golden sparks. Wielding it was Ogma, gentle poet and warrior-scholar. Sword and spell, the two gods strained themselves to the limit. It was Indech who held the advantage, however, for he was fated to win.

Forgotten in the shadows, however, was the Morrigan, a servant of Fate, who now betrayed that trust by severing the threads of providence that protected the Fomorian. The battle, preordained to bring Indech victory, ended with Ogma's blade through his heart. And so Indech died, thousands of years before his promised time, but his legacy would live on. Swearing vengeance, his son Octriallach turned into a white mist and fled into the forests of Winter. The victorious Tuatha de Danaan counted him among the dead; it was a mistake their changeling offspring would one day regret.

Scathach and the Sundering

The Fomorians were creatures of nightmare, but as they retreated a vital spark left the world. It was to this troubled era that Scathach's dynasty was born. Many of the Tuatha de Danaan departed the Autumn World, leaving the fae without their guidance; the Morrigan was among the first to go. Indech, she knew, had not been fated to die, but to play his part in the final times. The Morrigan had altered the edict of Fate and knew she had to pay the price. Before departing, she met one final time with Dagda. The two decided to spirit their child away to be raised on the island, Skye (the Isle of Shadows), that would one day bear her name. A sensible precaution, given what happened to both parents' previous children—Aedh, Mechi and poor haunted Leanhaun. Her affairs in order, the Morrigan transformed into a crow and flew deep into the Dreaming beyond all knowing. What she sought, and whether she found it, I cannot say.

Scathach grew up between two worlds, among the human villagers of Albion and a tribe of fuath who had remained loyal to the Tuatha de Danaan. Even as a child, she gained a great reputation as a warrior, hunter and sorceress. As a young adult she gained her greatest fame among outsiders as a teacher of martial arts to such celebrated individuals as the warrior Cu-Chulainn. It is fortunate that she was so capable, because the Old Ones' departure soon caused rifts that involved the young goddess. Ogma's descendants—among whom, I believe, you of House Gwydion consider yourselves—and the worshipers of the Morrigan vied to protect the Sword of Tethra. Tradition held that if Indech's blade was ever drawn again, it would signal the end of the Dreaming. At the very least, those foolish enough to touch it died horribly, their souls cast into howling darkness. The conflict was temporarily solved when the two sides agreed to protect it jointly in Caer Mathgen (in the once pleasant Blotkeldur Plains).

Even from the beginning, our philosophy of leadership differed from that of the other sidhe. Born to the purple, we initially ruled as tradition dictated, but the mantle of power didn't quite fit. I suppose this made us poor examples of the monarch's dream, but even then, the notion that we were entitled to control others' destinies simply by virtue of our blood troubled us. The

Morrigan had made the ultimate break with authority by refuting the patterns of Fate; her offspring were little different. Millennia passed and Scathach grew from warrior queen to something far more puissant and subtle. At her behest, we divested ourselves of all but a few strongholds, traveling through both Autumn World and Dreaming; we saw how the world was changing.

Even before the Shattering, various daring commoners underwent what has come to be known as the Changeling Way Ritual. Our house was hardly a trailblazer, but we were the only sidhe to make this momentous choice. Scathach herself was the first of our line to undergo the ritual, exchanging some of her nearly boundless power for the comparative mortality of human flesh—and the insights that came with it. The die was cast, and none too soon. The trials of the Sundering were as nothing compared with those to come.

The War of Trees

The War of Trees was the last time we openly fought alongside our fellow houses. After the Second Battle of Moytura, the Fomorians had returned and, with most Tuatha de Danaan gone, increasingly menaced the younger races. Eventually a time came when we had to choose sides. We laid our sword at Gwydion and Ailil's feet; the issues at stake were too important for our differences to stand in the way.

The conflict quickly escalated far beyond the scale set by the last war. We learned that Octriallach was not dead as once believed, but directing the cruelest of the Fomorian courts from deep within the Winterweir. A demon from our past had returned to haunt the world; our duty was clear. Since no army could hope to defeat a creature like Octriallach, Scathach herself—one of the few remaining Tuatha de Danaan, despite her diminished blood—led a disparate contingent of nobles and commoners into the Winterwoods.

The sun did not shine in those woods, and a never-ending host of Dark-kin, icy chimera and invisible spirits harried the invading host. Warriors disappeared into thin air, sometimes resurfacing as frozen, dismembered corpses. Still, the diminished company eventually reached the forest's chill heart and challenged the White King in his lair. Confident of his enemy's doom, Octriallach himself joined the fray, determined to capture Scathach alive and force from her the location of his father's blade.

The two met in single combat, and Scathach seemed a poor match for the White King, who warped and rent reality with his very presence. Bearing down upon his

Uathach

Scathach had a daughter. I'm sure you knew that much at least from our legends. It is hardly our best-kept secret, though the commonly told tale of her as a foil for Cu-Chulainn falls far short of her role in our house's traditions. No one in our tribe knows the identity of the father. Scathach kept her own counsel as to his identity, and at such times wisdom bade us discretion. It was obvious that she loved her daughter, perhaps too much. It is said that Uathach drew her name (literally meaning *the terrible*) from a prophecy by the old Tuathan wizard Mathgen, who served as Scathach's mentor and vizier. Even as a child, Uathach exhibited sorcerous skills that outstripped those of our clan's oldest magicians. And Scathach, ever indulgent of her daughter's desires, encouraged her in these Arts.

For the first seven years, daughter and mother were nigh inseparable. One winter's night, however, the Morrigan's granddaughter learned in a dream that she could take on the form of a sable unicorn. After that, she roamed far and wide, traveling roads forbidden to her by her mother. As she grew older, she became a rare beauty, attracting many would-be paramours, but all (including, eventually, Cu-Chulainn) came to bitter ends.

So it was in Uathach's twentieth year that Mathgen the wizard finally succumbed to the siren call of the other departed Old Ones and left for the Deep Dreaming. Uathach took his place as Malik and head of the Morphean Oracles, a position in our house second only to that of her mother. She grew in that role and, if she sometimes pursued unhealthy studies into the nature of the eldest of the Elder Darks, she also served our house loyally and well for centuries as her mother's right hand. Until, that is, Scathach decided that she and the rest of the tribe would undergo the Changeling Way. It is said that mother and daughter spoke harshly and that they even came to violence over the matter. Regardless, some short years before the War of Trees, Uathach and several like-minded followers departed for the Sea of Silver in pursuit of their destiny. What they sought, and if they found it, has been an enigma to even our greatest oracles, at least until now.

victim, the overconfident Fomorian did not notice how the Kithain's most potent sorcerers had arranged themselves into a complex wizard's knot around the battlefield, feeding their very life force into a fateful spell. The forest's trees writhed like tentacles, enveloping the shrieking White Court and imprisoning them within, seemingly forever. The task of defeating the Red and Green Courts lay ahead, but the fae would have to accomplish this with little aid from us. Scathach was gone, enshrined with her enemies at the heart of the Forest of Lies.

The Shattering

With the Fomorians' second defeat, the remaining Tuatha de Danaan departed for good. Following Scathach's last orders, we stayed behind to test ourselves against the chill winds of Banality, even as the other houses departed for Arcadia. We have never been ones to run from a fight, and we saw Banality as a foe no different from any other. As our fellow sidhe retreated, many commoners fell upon them in a murderous rage; even we were not immune. Nor was our house without sin. As we carried out the edicts of the Morphean Oracles, securing trods in the Near and Far Dreaming, some of us were not above seeking vengeance against the departing nobles.

Following the Second Battle of Moytura, the Sword of Tethra had lain under heavy guard at Caer Mathgen. With the War of Trees, however, the surrounding Blotkeldur had become a poisonous swamp. As House Gwydion departed the nearer Dreamrealms, the members insisted the sword accompany them to Arcadia. The Morphean Oracles foresaw calamity if the sword entered the Heart of the Dreaming, however, and we attacked as House Gwydion attempted to move it. During the ensuing bloodshed, the blade disappeared into the surrounding Dreaming. Did our seers, reputedly among the best in the Dreaming, not see this coming? I cannot say. Perhaps, despite the horror of Indech's blade being lost to that gloomy realm, they saw it as the lesser of two evils. With the White Court's recent awakening, we may soon learn the unpleasant truth in this matter.

The Interregnum

In this period we became both the hunters and the hunted. Our fellow sidhe abandoned us, and many changelings viewed us with suspicion. Nevertheless, our charge was clear: to protect the remaining fae and to prepare for the perils to come. With few friends among the Kithain, our attentions turned outward to those creatures known as *prodigals*. In the Autumn World we supported causes that fostered freedom, dignity and change within the human spirit—human suffering darkens the Dreaming and strengthens our ancient enemies. We've aided revolution, reform and abolitionist movements. In the Dreaming we wandered the Tenebrous Realms, guarding against incursions by the Dark-kin and far worse entities. In the end, we even earned back the trust of those commoners we helped, though most forgot about our very existence, consigning us to the ambiguities of myth.

Resurgence and Accord

Our oracles not only predicted the Resurgence in 1969, but the hour of your arrival. If the time of your appearance was clear, however, our reaction to it was less so. On one hand, here were the nobles who had abandoned and scorned us and who would soon wreak fire and death throughout Kithain society. On the other, here were sidhe, our long lost cousins, who would be desperately needed in the dark times ahead. We did what we could to help the returnees adjust to the new world and to avert the war that was fast approaching. We are not the only diviners of Fate, however; forces unknown skillfully hid the exact event that would spark the conflagration from us. When the Iron Knives Massacre lit the fuse, it was too late for us to stop the slaughter.

We offered our services to both sides, furthering our understandable, if erroneous, reputation as mercenaries. The commoners wanted information about the sidhe's tactics, while the nobles needed guidance in a strange new world. Neither suspected that we really served a third master, peace. We are a warrior house, but our ultimate goal is to save lives, not to take them. As always, we could only affect things at the fringes, our numbers being too small to force either side to the table. In the end, however, we saved some two hundred fae lives and helped shorten the war by six months. Every one of those lives will be needed in the times to come.

Things have hardly slowed since the war's end. Since then we've restored our contacts within Houses Fiona, Liam and Leanhaun. We have witnessed the 1980s Greens Rebellion in Europe (where our activities further irritated Dougal and Gwydion) and more recently the return of the Dark-kin and the remaining Arcadian houses. All signs point to the final days we have been awaiting, the beginning of Winter and the final days of House Scathach.

Silvered Dreams

You have come a long way to question me, but ever behind your queries I have heard the same unspoken concern. There were those of our house who did not remain during the Interregnum. There are those of us who never underwent the Changeling Way, but who followed Scathach's wayward daughter, Uathach, to the Silvered Sea. What of them? Some among us believe that, driven on by obscure portents and her own hubris, Uathach sought knowledge of the oldest of the Elder Darks, those of the so-called Emerald Dream. That even a powerful sorceress as she would dare to investigate beings to whom even our mightiest are as but gnats would seem absurd. Perhaps. But Uathach never had much appreciation for her limitations. I cannot say for certain what, if anything, she found, but I will tell you this. Some of her number, or perhaps their descendants, have arrived in the Near Dreaming (along with those of the other missing houses) and may even walk the streets of the Autumn World.

One of them has just made contact with our leaders in the Morphean Oracles. I know, because I was there. (I was returning from their home in Protea when you intercepted me.) He was accompanied by one of the Dark-kin, those called the keremet, and he had a lofty, unfocused air about him. Nevertheless, he exuded a raw power scarcely seen among even the oldest of you "true" sidhe. He restated the prodigal family's oaths of loyalty to our house (though, in truth, some among us questioned his veracity, shielded from our prophetic powers as he was). He offered Uathach's children's aid in strengthening the silver path, offering a convincing demonstration of their ability in this regard. He also stated, if I may deliver a veiled threat, that our prodigal family members are somewhat put out by the treatment of we Autumn Scathach at the hands of the other houses. I also believe I detected a certain ironic disdain for us in his words (perhaps I am merely being paranoid). I understand that in time the returnees may be paying a visit to members of the other houses to clarify the reasons for their presence, but for now their intentions (and the ultimate fate of Uathach) remain unknown even to us.

In the House of Shadows

(Sir Devyn Crow of House Balor explores the intricacies of Scathach honor)

Ah, thank you for loosening my bonds; they were beginning to chafe. Your proposal intrigues me, though I can't help but wonder what your companions would think about your offer to "spirit me away" from their intended justice. Maybe they'd just chalk it up to one misfit helping another? What you said is partially true, of course. Our houses do have much in common. Neither of us is truly sidhe, at least in any way that the other houses would consider meaningful. Many nobles see us as mere shadows of the true Shining Host, our existence as an affront to their very "sidhe-ness."

House Balor is growing in power, yes? We have watched your progress since the Resurgence, even as you have sought to monitor our activities. You wish to understand us? Be careful; we are not what you think. . .

On Nobility and Titles Lost

What does it mean to be born of the monarch's dream but to hold no sway? We sidhe are born from the dreams of rulership, but we are more than the sum of the beliefs that shape us. We have desires of our own. What occurs when such dreams reject their "appointed place" in the scheme of things? More than any other fae, noble or commoner, we have forged our own dreams. This is not to say that the loss of our noble standing does not sometimes sting. It also causes practical problems. Leading by example is more difficult and frequently less effective than simply taking command. Additionally, nobles and many commoners mistrust us as outsiders and impolitic meddlers. When we need it most, there is no safe haven for us.

This does not mean we are complete strangers to power. Once in a great while a Scathach hero may gain authority by unanimous acclaim from the fae of a community he has served. Except in the direst of circumstances, we refuse such honors. Scathach who seek power (as opposed to temporary leadership) amongst the commoners almost inevitably find their prestige within our house diminished. In the rare instances in which a Scathach noble takes a title, it is only for one generation and not a hereditary position. Sometimes the Morphean Oracles grant special dispensation to rule when it serves the house's needs. Usually, however, misfortune befalls those who break this ancient covenant.

Between Two Courts

We are as divided between our Seelie and Unseelie impulses as any fae, but we owe loyalty to neither court. While our original home was in the Seelie Court, we rejected such narrow loyalties when we underwent the Changeling Way Ritual. This led to some bitterness on the part of our Seelie brethren, many of whom took our departure as a personal insult. Conversely, it gave our Unseelie friends the idea that we were ripe for recruitment. House Scathach encourages its members to pursue their own interests and explore both philosophies, as long as they don't contravene the family's agenda. Our ultimate loyalty is to our house and its ideals.

The Morphean Oracles

The Morphean Oracles are the defining force within our house, and, even if we do not serve them without some reservation, they have our obedience. The Morphean Oracles have long resided in Protea, a minor Oneiric Realm bordering the Kingdom of Dán. The current oracles include the enigmatic phantom Talos of Protea, Birog the Lesser (Blue Witch of the Kureksarra Mountains) and a Modernist twentieth century addition, Celeste Vachon. The Morphean Oracles disseminate their will either through visions or more directly through their avatars, the khwaja dirigens. The only figure above the Oracles, excluding Scathach herself, is a shadowy figure known only as the Malik. Only three individuals throughout the house's history have held this position: The Tuathan wizard Mathgen, Scathach's daughter (Uathach) and currently a blind sorceress known only as Veleda.

Because we act largely as one, shunning the political machinations so rife in other houses, we are possibly the most cohesive body within Kithain society and free to act with great dispatch. Stemming directly from the Morrigan's teachings, our seers have both a special and, often, contrary relationship with Fate. We are adept at perceiving her grand design but do not see destiny as an immutable force. Rather than serving Fate's dictates, we seek to change certain threads in her tapestry (and have successfully done so on numerous occasions). Of course, this means that over the centuries, we have acquired Fate's wrath for our hubris. While this rarely affects our daily lives, it is no secret that the bill is coming due; our time is near an end. There are few of our number now, and soon there will be fewer still. This is the one aspect of Fate we *cannot* change (though some of us believe otherwise). In any event, we accept the danger. Whether we leave this world for better or for worse is the only question.

Of Allies, Equals and Adversaries

(Sir Fanchon ap Fiona learns of House Scathach's place in the world)

At last, a man of vision. I see you too are versed in the ways of Fate; it was you who led the others to me, was it not? You, more than your two companions, knew the dangers in coming to this frozen realm to capture me but you braved them just the same. Impressive. What do you seek? I have always had a fondness for House Fiona and, even though you are my jailer, I will aid you if I can. If, like your Balor colleague, you are here seeking an alliance, there is much you need to know. Let us play the old game, then, you and I. I will tell you a truth, then you will tell me one. Let us begin. . . .

Commoners

We have no illusions about our fellow changelings; over the past six hundred years we have seen them at their best and at their worst.

Boggans

In many ways the best of our kind, most boggans are levelheaded, kindly and know themselves—a rare commodity these days. Be careful about sharing secrets with them, however. Despite their best intentions, they are

The Hierarchy of House Mastery

Although House Scathach maintains some of its aristocratic trappings, its hierarchical system is unlike that of any other house. In short, it is a meritocracy, where even those with the richest blood and closest connections must start at the bottom. Unless the player buys the Merit: Mastery (see below), her character is a new fledge and starts out with no house mastery. Because of House Scathach's small numbers, there may be only a few sidhe at each level at any given time.

The minimum requirements listed below are just that. Having a score that exceeds these requirements does not guarantee the character an increase in rank. A fledge with Soothsay 5 may be a prodigy, but she has nowhere near the breadth of knowledge to wisely alter Fate at this point. Adherents to Scathach's path pursue physical, mental and spiritual mastery. Besides the requirements below, changelings of House Scathach frequently pursue the humanities (particularly history) and wilderness survival and—unlike most sidhe—keep abreast of human technological and social trends.

0 — **Fledge.** Scathach of this standing have just undergone the Chrysalis, are somewhere in the process of Fosterage and are discouraged from wandering unaccompanied. The sidhe's only responsibility at this point is to begin training. (Min. requirement: None)

1 — **Seeker** (Salik). The character has just undergone the Fior-Reigh and is a full, if provisional, member of the house. Scathach of this mastery may wander but are on a short leash and expected to report to a house sponsor. (Min. requirement: Brawl *or* Melee 1, Stealth 1)

2 — **Disciple** (Murid). The character has gained both some status and responsibilities, including monitoring less-experienced house members. (Min. requirement: Brawl *or* Melee 2, Changeling or Dreaming Lore 1, Gremayre 1, Stealth 2)

3 — **Fellow-Crafter.** Scathach at this level travel without supervision and are the backbone of the house's fighting forces. (Min. requirement: Brawl *or* Melee 3, Soothsay 1)

4 — **Knight.** Characters of this rank are called knights, carrying the honorific sir or lady, as one of the house's few nods to its aristocratic origins. Knights are the primary commanders within the warrior house but are restricted in policy matters. (Min. requirement: Gremayre 2, Changeling or Dreaming Lore 2, Stealth 3, Soothsay 2)

5 — **Enlightened One** (Arif). At this level, the character is assumed to have enough insights into Fate's tapestry to make minor decisions in manipulating its threads. (Min. requirement: Brawl *or* Melee 4, Changeling or Dreaming Lore 3, Gremayre 3, Stealth 4, Chronos 1, Soothsay 3)

6 — **Master** (Khwaja). The Khwaja is a roaming operative who seeks out major "defects" in Fate's tapestry. Very few Scathach are trusted with such a charge. (Min. requirement: Brawl *or* Melee 5, Changeling or Dreaming Lore 4, Gremayre 4, Stealth 5, Chronos 2, Soothsay 4)

7 — **Shadow** (Khwaja dirigens). The character undergoes the *Trial of Shadows*, becoming in effect a phantom presence in Fate's designs and a living avatar of the Morphean Oracles. There is only one Scathach of this rank on a continent and a few sprinkled throughout key Dreamrealms. (Min. requirement: Brawl *and* Melee 5, Changeling or Dreaming Lore 5, Gremayre 5, Chronos 5, Soothsay 5)

8 — **Oracle.** The character takes her place among the Morphean Oracles, the defining force within House Scathach.

9 — **Malik.** The Malik is the only authority above the Morphean Oracles. This was the place held by Scathach herself, and none have filled it since her disappearance during the War of Trees.

shameless gossips, almost on par with the blatherskites of House Daireann. Of course, we sometimes use this to our advantage. Share an inconvenient secret with a sluagh, and he'll sit on it until it suits him. Share one with a boggan, and it's all over the county by lunch.

Eshu

Along with the sluagh, eshu are the least frequently seen changelings; even we who share their road see them only rarely. Over the centuries we have forged a policy of mutual assistance, developing a vocabulary of symbols to indicate distance, trods and hidden dangers.

Nockers

Scathach was a patron goddess of blacksmiths and learned much from Skye's ubiquitous nocker population. We have some small talent in smithing, though nothing approaching the skills of this wily kith. Unlike most houses, we don't depend on them for our weapons.

Pooka

A fine kith in most respects. They know what it is to be both the hunter and the hunted. Unlike other sidhe, we are not immune to the pookas' pranking cantrips. After six hundred *long* years of dealing with them, we are not without humor, but consorting with pooka is enough to have even the best of us rethinking our rejection of noble status. They have taught us . . . patience. Despite our vulnerability to their pranks, most of them know not to push things too far. Once angered, we're not the easiest people in the world to placate.

Redcaps

With few exceptions, we have lost all trust for this kith. Many of them stayed on this side of the divide during the War of Trees but never fully severed their ties to the Midnight Host. As we guard against incursions from the Nightmare Realms, we are often as not battling redcaps.

Satyrs

Our existence is mostly a solitary one, and it is easy to become disconnected. The satyrs, more than any other, help to keep us grounded. Whether approaching them for lore or liaisons, we have found that underlying most satyrs' hedonism is a seriousness of purpose that rivals our own. Despite this, some of the Unseelie variety see our devotion to duty as a challenge and try to seduce us away from our responsibilities.

Sluagh

Because of our stealth and penchant for secrets, other houses have called us the most sluaghlike of the sidhe. I doubt this is meant as a compliment. Most sluagh distrust sidhe as a matter of course, and, despite centuries of proving otherwise, this suspicion still often pertains to us. Even so, we have found it useful to work with each other when our goals are aligned. Ironically, our diminished status among the other sidhe is our best asset when dealing with our fellow whisperers.

Trolls

Trolls make good allies and worthy adversaries. Both of us consider the protection of the other fae our duty, but we have split on how to fulfill these ends. Many trolls continue to support our fellow sidhe as leaders of the fae, and, while it is tempting to call such loyalists "lackeys," this is an oversimplification. Troll support, and the threat of its removal, has provided an invaluable check on destructive noble machinations within both courts.

Nobles

We have a mixed relationship with our fellow sidhe. They are blood-of-our-blood and we have no grudge against them as such. On the other hand, our beliefs have long ago put us in an adversarial relationship with most houses.

The Seelie Court

We were once affiliated with this court, and even now most of us are more sympathetic to Seelie sensibilities. On the other hand, recent Seelie domination of the Autumn fae has caused an unhealthy imbalance in the Dreaming, one we will soon rectify.

House Beaumayn

As fellow prophets and wanderers of the French countryside, we have been both allied and at odds with this house, but never enemies. They were apparently imprisoned while in Arcadia. Like us, they now share the enmity of the other houses; we must learn more of this.

House Dougal

Those of House Dougal are our superiors in matters of crafting; we acknowledge these skills but little else. They are honorable and may be approached as such on an individual basis, though Balor spies in their ranks make this a dicey proposition. As a house, they are far too invested in supporting House Gwydion. Until this changes, we are unlikely to be friends.

with us that stems from their Volva tradition. Their warriors are among the best I've seen, and their Volvas approach our seers' prophetic abilities.

House Ailil

Ironically, the most fluent schemers among the Unseelie Court have been our greatest assets when crossing the Shadow Court's designs. Ailil politics may be nigh impenetrable, but we have little difficulty in recognizing where our objectives coincide. Most of this house realize that when the Elder Darks return, the best even they can hope for is the status of favored slaves. To this end, despite their patrician arrogance, we have let them "cultivate" us as a hedge against House Balor.

House Balor

Despite your companion's overtures, the chances of us allying ourselves with the Serpent House are considerably smaller than those of my flapping my arms and flying to the moon. Yes, we share a certain outcast status, but the similarity ends there. They offer us "revenge on and power over" the Seelie fae when their Fomorian progenitors sweep them to victory. How little they understand us. It is possible their dark kind may one day inundate the world, but House Scathach will ever oppose them.

House Daireann

We have an "interesting" relationship with the Oaken House. The progeny of two puissant warrior queens, our houses have been fierce rivals since the beginning and on opposite sides of more than one battlefield. Even so, our relationship has always been one more of rivalry than hate. This feud began when a garrulous member of House Daireann revealed our ally Cu-Chulainn's weakness— ironically to a renegade avatar of the Morrigan—resulting in his death. We are pragmatic about such issues, however, and have no desire to spill fresh blood over so ancient a grudge.

House Leanhaun

If you go back far enough, all sidhe are related through the Tuatha de Danaan, but we have a special connection with the house of Scathach's half sister. Intelligent, mercurial, cultured and cruel, the House of Thorns has long had our admiration, if not our approval. Unfortunately, their family's curse weighs heavily on them, their desperation inexorably compelling them toward an unknown darkness. No doubt remains that we are on a collision course, but whether our ultimate destiny is to die in aiding or destroying them, I cannot say. No matter what, we are close kin and find them intriguing. For now, we can sympathize with their plight and enjoy their company without falling prey to their wiles.

House Varich

We know little about this Russian house, but what we have seen disturbs us. They are weavers of patterns and control the spirits of field and hearth. They also seem to have an unhealthy interest in the dark winter chimera who appear ever more numerously at our borders. Yet, they are a proud house and may wish to stay free of the Elder Darks. Fate obscures their final role. We will watch, wait and, when necessary, act.

Adhene

More than almost any other fae, we have gained experience with these children of the Fomorian Dream. When we encounter them, it is almost inevitably as enemies. We have some small sympathy for the neutral Adhene—Scathach herself was raised by fuath. We have

also made tentative alliances with the muses and some independent agencies among the keremet and fir-bholg, but those who worship the Fomorian Dream can expect no quarter. Owing to our less than sanguine view of Fate as immutable, the moiræ do not much care for us, viewing us as "loose threads" in Fate's tapestry. We are wild cards, and the vassals of Fate do not like surprises.

Fomorians

Think what you want of us, about our diluted blood, repudiation of your traditions and propensity to stick our noses where they do not belong. It is all to one end. The Elder Darks are awake and even now shape the world to their alien appetites. The White Court has freed itself of its arboreal prison, but Scathach, imprisoned with them, has disappeared. We are not a vengeful house by nature, nor do I boast, but if she is dead, *no* force in existence will stay our wrath. Fomorian or not, the White Court will choke on its own nightmares. Fate tells us that the world will soon plunge into night everlasting and we, foolish half-breeds, are just arrogant enough to question her prophecies. These are the times for which we were born.

Sir Fanchon,

I beg your forgiveness for this rejection of your hospitality, but my mission calls and I can spend no more time among you, no matter how pleasant the company.

Lady Victoria is trussed up in the back of the cart. Attacking an opponent from behind goes against my grain, but I imagine it is preferable to what Sir Devyn had in store for you both. Check his bags and you will find a quantity of eye blight, a favorite of assassins in the Eyes of Balor. The poison wouldn't have killed you, but it would have rotted your eyes right out of their sockets. You will find Sir Devyn at the bottom of the nearby precipice.

I wish you luck in defending your keep. I regret that our paths take us in different directions for the moment, but we will meet again. House Scathach always seems to be on the side of the underdog and, in the coming storm, we will stand by your side. Draw what comfort from this as you may.

Yours,
Jolanthe ap Scathach

The Warrior's Halo (House Scathach Martial Arts)

Scathach herself was a renowned martial artist, and the fighting style she passed on to her descendants is a synthesis of mind, body, spirit and Glamour. To learn a martial feat, the character must have at least an equal number of dots in either Brawl (for unarmed feats) or Melee (for armed feats) as the level of the feat she wishes to learn. The cost for each feat is x1 freebie points (or x2 experience) the level listed below.

Unarmed Feats

Whirl of the Chariot Chief (Level 1)

This move is as ancient as it is simple: Grab, spin, throw. The warrior may choose to throw his opponent directly to the ground or hurl her away from him.

Roll: Dexterity + Brawl

Difficulty: 7 (8 for sidhe vs. troll, or childling vs. wilder or grump)

Damage: Strength

System: A thrown opponent must make a contested Dexterity + Athletics roll (difficulty 6). Failure means she loses her remaining actions that turn or suffers +2 difficulty to actions the next turn (if she has already acted). Those who succeed must still add +1 difficulty to any actions they attempt that turn. The warrior throws his foe 5 feet for each success.

The Hero's Salmon Leap (Level 2)

The character can jump her maximum distance vertically or horizontally, carrying whatever or whomever she wishes (as long as the burden's weight doesn't exceed her Strength's carry maximum).

System: No roll is required; the character simply succeeds. This feat requires 1 point of Glamour.

Cantrip Combination: The character gains an automatic extra success on the Wayfare cantrip *Hopscotch* and may choose to break one long leap into multiple short leaps with a Dexterity + Athletics roll. (Difficulty 7, one leap per success; the cumulative area covered may not exceed the character's maximum distance for a single leap.)

Running up the Lance (Level 3)

After a successful dodge, the character runs up the attacker's weapon to deliver her counterattack.

Roll: Dexterity + Dodge

Difficulty: 6

Damage: Strength + Weapon

System: With this feat, the character dodges her attacker and leaps upon his weapon, adding two dice to the counterattack. Furthermore, this feat requires the target to make a Strength + Melee roll (difficulty 6). Failing to match or exceed his opponent's number of successes means the target loses his weapon. Size makes no difference when using this feat; a grump troll could as easily stand on the end of a childling's blade as the reverse. This feat requires 1 point of Glamour and lasts one turn.

Hero's Twisting Around the Spear (Level 4)

Using this feat, the character charges toward those using ranged weapons, closing the distance and arriving close enough to engage in melee the *next* turn.

Roll: Dexterity + Dodge

Difficulty: 6 (+1 per extra opponent)

Damage: None

System: The character gives up all actions besides the feat. In the Dreaming the character covers an additional x1 his maximum distance per success. (A single success adds 50 percent to the character's speed.) The Autumn World demands that the warrior call upon the wyrd or else move "only" a maximum of double her normal speed. This feat requires 1 point of Glamour and lasts one turn.

The Shaman's Fire Walking Feat (Level 4)

This feat protects the warrior from fire.

Roll: Stamina + Survival

Difficulty: 7

Damage: None

System: Each success reduces fire damage by 1 point. This feat requires 1 point of Glamour and lasts one turn per success. Exceptionally hot fires (dragonfire, napalm, etc.) require an additional point of Glamour.

Breaking the King's Crown (Level 5)

Although House Scathach has surrendered its rulership and right to use Sovereign, this does not mean that they allow others to use them as pawns. This martial feat represents such a degree of mental mastery that the user can resist the Sovereign Art and other forms of mind control.

Roll: Willpower

Difficulty: 7

Damage: None

System: Each success reduces the number of successes scored against the warrior by 1 point. This feat requires 1 point of Glamour.

Armed Feats

Throw the Staff (Level 1)

The character throws a staff (spear, baseball bat, pool cue, etc.), aiming low in an attempt to unbalance his target.

Roll: Dexterity + Melee

Difficulty: Weapon +1

Damage: Weapon

System: An opponent hit by the thrown staff must make a contested Dexterity + Athletics roll (difficulty 6). Failure means she loses her remaining actions that turn or suffers +2 difficulty to actions the next turn (if she has already acted). Those who succeed must still add +1 difficulty to any actions they attempt that turn.

Cantrip Combination: If the caster uses the Legerdemain cantrip *Ensnare* upon the weapon, the character may attempt to knock down one foe per cantrip success.

The Shield Rim Feat (Level 2)

After a successful shield parry, the wielder may attempt a standard weapon attack *plus* an unsporting riposte with the hard rim of her shield.

Roll: Dexterity + Melee

Difficulty: Weapon

Damage: Weapon

System: The character must split her dice pool for the second two actions, but both the weapon *and* the shield benefit from the Boon of House Scathach.

The Musket Duel Feat (Level 3)

When involved in a gunfight, the warrior may cloak himself in the gun smoke.

Roll: Dexterity + Stealth

Difficulty: Variable

Damage: None

System: This feat requires someone in the near vicinity to discharge some kind of firearm; the "dirtier" the weapon the better. A cannon or flame-thrower might be difficulty 4, while an old-style flintlock is difficulty 6. Comparatively smokeless modern weapons may be difficulty 8 or 9. Numerous weapons in the area decrease the difficulty. For each success the Scathach character scores, his opponent loses one die against him the next turn (as long as their action requires that they see him). Multiple successes can be divided among multiple opponents. Because this is a warrior's feat, only weapon smoke will do. This feat requires 1 point of Glamour.

The Thunder Feat (Level 4)

The character throws a small, blunt weapon (club, rock, sling-stone) into her opponents. The weapon bursts with a clap of thunder, and all in the targeted area take damage.

Roll: Dexterity + Melee

Difficulty: Weapon -1

Damage: Weapon

System: The radius of effect is 5 feet per success. This feat requires 1 point of Glamour, and damage is consistent throughout the blast area.

Cantrip Combination: When used with the Primal cantrip *Holly Strike* and the proper Realm, the cantrip damage is added to the weapon damage. Only things of that Realm take extra damage, however. Targets not of that Realm take only the feat's standard damage.

The Scythe Chariot Feat (Level 5)

The character leaps into the air, spinning in a savage blur and attacking with one weapon per hand. She neither splits her dice pool nor suffers from an off-hand penalty.

Roll: Dexterity + Melee

Difficulty: Weapon

Damage: Weapon

System: This feat requires 1 point of Glamour.

Cantrip Combination: When used with the Wayfare cantrip *Quicksilver*, the true power of this feat becomes apparent. Whereas a normal fae might gain three actions, a character using the scythe chariot feat could gain up to six attacks (if she has the Glamour to cover all three feats). Such remarkable destruction has led some Scathach down the road to Bedlam. . . .

Commoner Feats

Developed by Scathach herself, the Oath of the Honor Bound Allies (see Merits below) allows the user to teach a commoner either unarmed or armed skills, permanently giving the student +1 die on either her Melee *or* Brawl dice pools. The commoner, in turn, shares a bit of her Birthright. The Scathach character loses his house Boon against all members of the kith to which he has sworn the oath; the commoner does not get the new combat bonus against members of House Scathach.

Members of the kith listed below may buy their own kith's feat at 1 freebie point (or 2 experience points) below cost, while they may buy feats belonging to other kith at 1 freebie point (or 2 experience points) above the listed cost (provided a member of House Scathach is there to perform the Rite). The Storyteller is the final arbiter of what feats a player can buy in this manner.

If either party breaks this oath or commits deliberately vile deeds (cold-blooded murder, oath breaking, and so on) against *any* member of the allied house or kith, he breaks the pact and loses any benefits he gained from it. Only the oath breaker loses these benefits; the other party to the pact retains her honor. The violator also permanently gains +1 difficulty to all future Charisma or Manipulation rolls when dealing with members of the offended kith, at least until he makes serious restitution (often a quest in and of itself).

The Jaw Feat (Level 1)

Taught by redcaps (very rarely), this unarmed feat allows the character to stretch her jaws impossibly wide, turning her face into a frightening visage.

Roll: Strength + Brawl

Difficulty: 6

Damage: Strength + 2

System: The practitioner gains +1 die on all Intimidation rolls, plus she can do bite damage at *almost* the same level as a redcap (the damage difficulty is a standard 6, compared to the redcap's difficulty of 5). No limb severing or eating nonedible material allowed, however; such things are solely the province of the redcap. This unarmed feat requires 1 point of Glamour and lasts one turn per success.

The Long-Arm Feat (Level 2)

The character can stretch his body parts æ neck, legs, arms, whatever.

Roll: Dexterity + Athletics

Difficulty: 7

Damage: None

System: Effects could be variable: +1 initiative die if one were to stretch an arm out for a quick attack, +1 die on wrestling moves or to escape (Storyteller's decision). A changeling may not use this feat in the presence of unenchanted nonfae. This unarmed feat requires 1 point of Glamour and lasts one turn per success.

The Charioteer Goad Feat (Level 3)

This feat allows a character to heap verbal abuse upon his weapon until it, eager to prove its wielder wrong, attacks or parries foes on its own.

Roll: Manipulation + Intimidation

Difficulty: 7

Damage: Weapon (roll Manipulation rather than Strength)

System: The character makes a Manipulation + Intimidation roll; the number of successes is the dice pool for the weapon's attack. Because this feat requires some direction, the caster is –1 to his dice pool for the feat's duration. This armed feat requires 1 point of Glamour and lasts one turn per success. Autumn World weapons require the character to call upon the wyrd.

The Disrespectful Left Side of the Chariot Feat (Level 3)

Taught by the pooka, the warrior physically or verbally taunts her target so fiercely that he becomes cross and makes a mistake.

Roll: Manipulation + Persuasion

Difficulty: The target's Willpower +4 (maximum 10)

Damage: None

System: Each success translates to –1 die from her opponent's Perception pool (minimum 2). This feat requires 1 point of Glamour and lasts one turn per success. This unarmed feat can be used only against a single target, and each future attempt against that opponent reduces the feat's efficacy by one success.

The Tongue of the Satirist Feat (Level 3)

House Scathach leads by deeds, not words (though some Scathach sidhe are excellent orators). The ehsu can teach the skill of glib oration like none other, giving the student additional skills in the volatile arena of wordplay.

Roll: Manipulation or Charisma + Leadership or Persuasion

Difficulty: 8

Damage: None

System: Not necessarily a combat feat, this ability lowers the difficulty by 1 point for any Persuasion or Leadership rolls. This armed or unarmed feat requires 1 point of Glamour and lasts one half hour per success.

The Apple Feat (Level 4)

This is the classic "show-off" combat skill. Taught by the boggans, this feat allows the character to make an attack plus one extra *noncombat* action per turn without splitting her dice pool. The famous boggan chef, Deuce "Hasty" Blancmange, is said to have prepared a seven-course meal while holding off a coterie of hungry redcaps in this manner. Note that if engaged in melee combat, characters have only one hand free with which to work.

Roll: Dexterity + Athletics

Difficulty: 7

Damage: None

System: The action's complexity is the key concept here. Flipping a switch is a simple task; defusing a bomb is not (though the latter may be performed with increased difficulty and multiple accumulated successes). The Storyteller has the final say on what deeds are possible with this feat. This unarmed feat requires 1 point of Glamour and lasts one turn per success.

Cantrip Combination: When used with the Wayfare cantrip *Quicksilver*, the caster still gains only one additional *noncombat* action from this feat per turn.

The Respectful Right Side of the Chariot Feat (Level 5)

This potent troll feat allows the warrior to force an "honorable truce" with an opponent, temporarily forcing the adversary to cease hostilities.

Roll: Manipulation + Empathy

Difficulty: 6

Damage: None

System: The caster's roll is a contested one against the target's permanent Willpower (difficulty 6). If the caster gains more successes, the target must suspend hostilities for the remainder of the scene. Subsequent uses against an enemy reduce the caster's dice pool by 1 point per attempt. A warrior who casts this rite and then violates the treaty to gain a temporary advantage over an enemy gains 1 permanent point of Banality and temporarily loses 2 points of Strength (to a minimum of 1) as the Dreaming exacts its revenge. This armed or unarmed feat requires 1 point of Glamour.

New Background

House Scathach is a meritocracy with rank based solely on accomplishment. Although there are 11 levels of merit in Scathach society, beginning player characters cannot go higher than the fifth level. Clearly, a player may not buy a rank higher than the minimum requirements for that level of mastery (see "The Hierarchy of House Mastery" above). Characters without this Background are mere fledges, though a Storyteller should grandfather a longtime player character to an appropriate level within the hierarchy.

1 dot — Salik (Seeker)

2 dots — Murid (Disciple)

3 dots — Fellow Crafter

4 dots — Knight

5 dots — Arif (Enlightened One)

New Merits

Oracle (4 Points)

Except for the moiræ and the sidhe of House Beaumayn, the seers of House Scathach are quite possibly the best in the Dreaming. This is a birthright handed down through the generations from the Morrigan herself, giving the character –2 difficulty on all rolls involving the Soothsay Art. This Merit is not exclusive to House Scathach, but is possessed by the most able prophets of other kith and houses. Because most others don't share Scathach's prophetic heritage, however, the cost is +1 freebie point for all other fae except for the moiræ and House Beaumayn.

Oath of the Honor-Bound Allies (5 Points)

Where sidhe with Sovereign command obedience, Scathach with this ritual forge alliances. This oath is exchanged only when a member of the house has done a great favor for a commoner or vice versa. Each Kithain involved in the transaction must exchange blood and spend 1 point of temporary Glamour. Only Scathach's descendants may master this potent ritual, and the caster must have at least Fae 2 (Lofty Noble) and Gremayre 3 to learn its intricacies. The cost for casting this rite is 1 point of Glamour; thus, if the caster is also party to the exchange, she must spend 2 points of Glamour (one to cast the spell and the other to seal her half of the oath).

Phantom Fate (5 Points)

Fate's tapestry records the life and destiny of every living being. Most lives are stitched in bright and vivid threads, easy for Fate's disciples to watch and record. Others, however, are recorded in threads invisible to all but the most discerning eye. Because House Scathach has taken up a contrarian relationship to Fate's design, some have become truly adept at camouflaging their patterns. Such "ciphers" are all but invisible to the Soothsay cantrip *Omen* (the only way to track such a character is by deciphering the "ripples" she causes when she interacts with others). Furthermore, all other Soothsay cantrips are at +3 difficulty when cast against her, though this additional difficulty pertains to beneficial and detrimental effects alike. The character is just as likely to deflect blessings as curses and may not purchase any Merits or Flaws pertaining to luck.

Scathach who attain the seventh level of mastery undergo a rite known as the Trial of Shadows and automatically exhibit this Merit—if they survive. This Merit is not exclusive to House Scathach (indeed, even

some humans may unwittingly be ciphers) but is quite rare elsewhere. The cost is +2 freebie points for all other fae. Moiræ may not purchase this Merit and are particularly antipathetic toward those so endowed.

Birthrights and Frailties

Scathach's Birthrights and Frailties have changed somewhat since the house's first appearance in **Nobles: The Shining Host.**

Birthrights

Awe and Beauty — The beauty of the sidhe is somewhat diluted by the Changeling Way Ritual. Scathach sidhe receive only 1 additional point instead of the usual 2. (The Attribute may still exceed 5.) Note that this does not apply to those Scathach who have just returned from Arcadia.

Noble Bearing — Like most sidhe, those of House Scathach have a raw nobility but no defense against cantrips making them look foolish. This weakened Birthright still means that no Scathach sidhe will ever botch an Etiquette roll. Scathach just returned from Arcadia do not have this weakened birthright.

Frailties

Blood Madness — Because of their changeling nature, sidhe of this house do not suffer from Banality's Curse. They do, however, exhibit a strange madness in battle. Although a member of this house will not attack friends or bystanders, she has great difficulty leaving combat until either she, or all her enemies, are defeated, though not necessarily dead or even unconscious. (She may accept an honorable surrender.)

To leave a conflict, the player must make a Willpower roll (difficulty 7) and accumulate six successes before retreating. A botch returns this count to its starting point, and the warrior must wait a full turn before attempting to retreat again. A character may burn 1 point of Willpower for only one automatic success during this process. Unlike in the Gwydion Flaw, Scathach in this state take all the usual Health penalties when injured. A Scathach warrior becomes preternaturally silent during combat and has great difficulty speaking above a whisper. To speak more loudly the character must make a Willpower roll (difficulty 7) and may utter one short phrase per success. Recent returnees are subject to this frailty just as their more "common" house members.

Boons and Flaws

Boon: Those of House Scathach are silent and efficient warriors. They rarely make any sound when fighting, causing great consternation in their foes. Once entering a fight, they lose sight of almost everything else, reaching a hypnotic "fugue state" in which the world seems to move more slowly. Because of the perceived time crawl in this state, they receive an extra die on all Brawl and Melee rolls and make Stealth rolls at -1 difficulty. Recent returnees also enjoy this boon.

Ban: Most nobles look down upon House Scathach. All Social rolls with other sidhe (except Houses Beaumayn, Fiona, Liam and Leanhaun) *and* commoners with strong royalist sympathies are at +2 difficulty (or up to +4 with Traditionalist nobles). Furthermore, because of an ancient blood pact, Scathach are forbidden to use the Art of Sovereign. This ban is enforced by the full weight of the Dreaming. Scathach who have just returned from Arcadia still suffer from the Social difficulties of their house members if those with whom they are interacting know their house affiliation. They are not forbidden to use the Sovereign Art as are their Autumn Scathach counterparts.

Affinity: Nature

A House Divided: Autumn vs. Arcadian Scathach

There has been some speculation about whether the Dreaming still treats Scathach sidhe as nobles or if it now considers them commoners. Herewith, the answer.

Those who have recently returned are now being called Arcadian Scathach while members of the house who remained on Earth are known as Autumn Scathach. This latter name is for ease in telling them apart only! Try calling one an Autumn Scathach and see how fast you regret doing so.

Born to the Purple

According to sidhe of other houses, all members of House Scathach have betrayed their aristocratic heritage and are now no better than any other common rabble. The Dreaming, however, seems to have a different opinion—at least so far as Scathach recently returned from

Arcadia are concerned. When casting a cantrip that affects an Arcadian Scathach, the caster must employ Fae 2 (Lofty Noble), just like he would against a noble of any other house. This has led some nobles of other houses to believe that House Scathach is not completely beyond redemption, while at the same time bolstering their royalist contention that this proves the Dreaming favors the sidhe as the fae's true rulers. The Dreaming, they argue, does not permit those born to the "chosen kith" to escape the duties and privileges of rulership. At the same time, some commoners view this as proof that those of House Scathach, despite their strong commoner sympathies, are ultimately still aristocrats and, as such, cannot be fully trusted.

Fallen Lords

When those of House Scathach who remained behind renounced their right to rule and underwent the Changeling Way Ritual, they gave up far more than most Kithain suspect. Whether as a conscious choice or a penalty imposed by Fate, the Dreaming

or a conclave of other houses (histories vary), the Dreaming reflects the house's fallen station on the most fundamental level. When casting a cantrip that affects an Autumn Scathach, the caster employs Fae 1 (Hearty Commoner), just like she would against any other commoner. To most nobles, this is damning proof of the house's inferior status; a changeling so easily affected by another's Arts is hardly worthy of the lofty title of sidhe. Conversely, commoners who know of this apparent weakness view House Scathach's sacrifice in this regard (along with the house's reduction of sidhe beauty and revocation of Sovereign) as convincing evidence of the house's commoner credentials.

Those who have met both Arcadian and Autumn Scathach and had any cause to cast cantrips on them may be quite confused, for this shortcoming is not common knowledge. The few sidhe who have realized it are now quite concerned with their own status. No one yet knows what happens to sidhe killed in the Autumn Realm. If they do reincarnate, perhaps through a Wake being held for them, will they return as commoners akin to the Autumn Scathach or as some other form of commoner? Or will they fail to return at all? Some would no doubt prefer death to the dishonor of such a fall from their noble status.

APPENDIX: CHARACTER TEMPLATES

Thallain Hunter of House Beaumayn

Quote: *There it is! Don't let it get away!*

Background: Life has always been a storybook tale for you . . . one of the original tales, that is, from the days before stories were cleaned up for a skittish public, one of the tales in which the monster just might win. Growing up on a small farm in a remote hill region of southern France, as far back as you can remember the days were separated by the stories from Father's antique, leather-bound book. Every night you heard a different tale, so vivid you felt you were actually part of each one. It was these stories that first awakened your faerie nature, but your Chrysalis was a mixed blessing at best, as you quickly learned. For even before your fae nature emerged, you always knew that there were monsters after you—shapeless horrors gnashing their teeth under the bed, nightmare men with lurid knives lurking in the closet, dire wolves stalking just beyond the trees. But while the other children only shivered at such tales, your monsters were real, their were claws cut, their words gave you nightmares and they never, *ever* went away for long. What's worse, only Father seemed to see them like you did, and even he couldn't stop them from harming you, only soothe the worst of the pain. You can only imagine the agony that he went through, watching you suffer and powerless to help you. Much of your early childhood is little more than a blur from the constant Mists these creatures drove you into, and your nightmares still recall many long nights spent huddled in your family's tiny farmhouse, hoping whatever thing was outside would leave you alone.

But you didn't suffer entirely in vain. Father wasn't simply reading you old stories for the sake of enjoyment; he was actually a kinain trying as best he could to educate his poor child on the weaknesses of these creatures. Folklore is a treasure trove of such details, for those clever enough to realize it, and you were an able student. You learned the weak points of your tormentors one by one, and by the time you were twelve you were an expert at fighting things that would turn the stomachs of redcaps twice your age. Soon the dark things learned to scurry at your approach, though the bravest ones still try to make as much trouble for you as they can from outside the reach of your sword. When you were a little older still and it came time to leave the farm, Father gave you his book, all the traveling money your parents could spare and a chimerical sword given to him by your grandfather; you haven't gone back since. Meeting other changelings was something of a shock after your isolated upbringing, and you've had to deal with your share of scorn for wearing your house colors so openly. You have adjusted as best you can and even begun making a name for yourself as an eminently capable hunter of all things dire and chimerical.

When word traveled of the twins gathering members of the House in New Orleans, you knew the call you had been waiting for all your life had been sounded at last. Arranging a study abroad program that would take you to the States wasn't difficult once you got in touch with them, and your dedication and intelligence has made the international transition an easy one so far. You have quickly come to realize that Concordia is even more rife with the foul Thallain and their ilk than your homeland, but this doesn't worry you overmuch. Slaying them is the easy part, after all; awakening the other Kithain to the threat among them and leading them to action is where your task becomes difficult. So far you've been traveling wherever your current motley will take you, seeking out creatures of darkness to destroy and trying to leave the local Kithain better prepared to root out such vileness in the future.

It is lonely work, and more than one motley has scattered in the wake of your more dangerous hunts, but no matter. You've worked alone before, and you still have plenty of scars and sleepless nights that need avenging.

Roleplaying Hints: You are a true professional, cool and collected under fire and with a good head for giving the right orders to the right people at just the right time. While not exactly arrogant, your upbringing in Neustria (as the Kithain know France) and its staunchly pro-monarchy attitudes have colored your outlook more than you realize, which can get you into trouble with the more egalitarian Concordian fae, especially commoners. A walking fountain of Thallain lore, you don't call attention to your Beaumayn lineage but don't hide it either. If others have a problem with it, that's their concern, as long as they don't interfere with the hunt. Show no sign of the trauma you endured as a childling, at least not until you have one of the foul beasts at bay. You do not believe in torture, but a suffering Thallain doesn't concern you much either. You've already suffered worse scars than most adults have at the age of forty, and payback is sweet indeed.

Equipment: Battered sword, antique book of faerie tales, French-English dictionary.

Book of Lost Houses: The Second Coming

Name: _____   **Court:** *Seelie*   **Seeming:** *Wilder*
Player: _____   **Legacies:** *Knight/Shade*   **Kith:** *Sidhe*
Chronicle: _____   **House:** *Beaumayn*   **Motley:** _____

Attributes

Physical
Strength ●●●●○
Dexterity ●●●●○
Stamina ●●●○○

Social
Charisma ●●●●○
Manipulation ●○○○○
Appearance ●●●●○

Mental
Perception ●●●●○
Intelligence ●●●●○
Wits ●●●○○

Abilities

Talents
Alertness ●●●●○
Athletics ○○○○○
Brawl ●●○○○
Dodge ●●●○○
Empathy ○○○○○
Intimidation ●●○○○
Kenning ●●●●○
Persuasion ○○○○○
Streetwise ○○○○○
Subterfuge ○○○○○

Skills
Crafts ○○○○○
Drive ○○○○○
Etiquette ○○○○○
Firearms ○○○○○
Leadership ●●○○○
Melee ●●●○○
Performance ○○○○○
Security ○○○○○
Stealth ●○○○○
Survival ●○○○○

Knowledges
Computer ○○○○○
Enigmas ●●○○○
Gremayre ●●●●●
Investigation ●●○○○
Law ○○○○○
Linguistics ●○○○○
Lore ●●○○○
Medicine ●○○○○
Politics ○○○○○
Science ○○○○○

Advantages

Backgrounds
Chimera (Sword) ●●○○○
Remembrance ●●●○○
Treasure (Storybook) ●●●○○
_____ ○○○○○
_____ ○○○○○

Arts
Primal ●●○○○
Wayfare ●●●○○
_____ ○○○○○
_____ ○○○○○
_____ ○○○○○

Realms
Actor ●○○○○
Fae ●●●●○
_____ ○○○○○
_____ ○○○○○
_____ ○○○○○

Other Traits
_____
_____
_____
_____
_____
_____

Glamour
●●●●●○○○○○
☐☐☐☐☐☐☐☐☐☐

Willpower
●●○○○○○○○○
☐☐☐☐☐☐☐☐☐☐

Ravaging/Musing Threshold

Banality
●●●○○○○○○○
☐☐☐☐☐☐☐☐☐☐

Health

		Real	Chimerical
Bruised		☐	☐
Hurt	-1	☐	☐
Injured	-1	☐	☐
Wounded	-2	☐	☐
Mauled	-2	☐	☐
Crippled	-5	☐	☐
Incapacitated		☐	☐

Birthrights/Frailties

Experience: ☐

Third-Millennium Volva of House Aesin

Quote: *I can see that your hands are immersed with innocent blood. I am glad that you approached me. Only I can help you clean them.*

Background: Once a charlatan and social lowlife, you have found meaning in your existence. The fame you received when a mortal saw your true appearance as your ancient soul manifested itself in impure flesh has caused you to be the hottest name among high-ranking members of the wealthy community. Rumor has it that you actually managed to contact a soul during the séance and allowed it to use you as host, or, in other words, you are the real thing! Fact is, it was no ghost. The young mortal witnessed your rebirth into mortal flesh. Still, you enjoy the attention you're getting. Back in the old days you got a piece of bread or some small jewels. Now they give you every material thing you desire only to get you to appear at one of their social gatherings. These wealthy mortals might come in handy when the Dream War begins in earnest. They can probably provide you with what is necessary to survive Ragnarök.

The downside is that the media have their eyes on you as well. After all, you are the rich people's little pet. You wander among freeholds and offer your soothsaying services to gullible mortals. People know you to be a nonsocial person. They can sense the contempt you have for them, but they dare not say anything. For who can tell what a powerful medium as you can do? There are those who have offered you a place in secret societies, but each time you have rejected them, even scorned them as fools. Meanwhile you harvest Glamour from the fools who acquire your services and build an Aesin empire your way, not through the "Ragnelf way."

Roleplaying Hints: There are those who call you superficial, a snob and an enigma. Of course, they are all correct. These are the words that define your personality. No matter what you do, you always let the customer see that you are so much more than he is. Others' opinions are worth nothing. They come back for more anyway. When dealing with fellow nobles, you have a tendency to act more on the enigma personality. You provide your service but let your clients know little of you. Nevertheless, you are very aware that you have deviated from the common Aesin path—you lie, cheat and manipulate.

This is the sidhe's world, and you are enjoying the playground before the restoration comes.

Equipment: Wooden staff, small rune stones, cellular phone, business cards.

Book of Lost Houses: The Second Coming

Name: _____ Court: *Unseelie* Seeming: *Grump*
Player: _____ Legacies: *Riddler/Dandy* Kith: *Sidhe*
Chronicle: _____ House: *Aesin* Motley: _____

Attributes

Physical
Strength _____ ●●○○○
Dexterity _____ ●●●●○
Stamina _____ ●●●●○

Social
Charisma _____ ●●●○○
Manipulation _____ ●●●●○
Appearance _____ ●●●○○

Mental
Perception _____ ●●○○○
Intelligence _____ ●●●○○
Wits _____ ●●○○○

Abilities

Talents
Alertness _____ ●●○○○
Athletics _____ ○○○○○
Brawl _____ ●○○○○
Dodge _____ ●●○○○
Empathy _____ ●●○○○
Intimidation _____ ○○○○○
Kenning _____ ●●●○○
Persuasion _____ ○○○○○
Streetwise _____ ○○○○○
Subterfuge _____ ●●●○○

Skills
Crafts _____ ○○○○○
Drive _____ ○○○○○
Etiquette _____ ●●○○○
Firearms _____ ○○○○○
Leadership _____ ●●○○○
Melee _____ ●●●○○
Performance _____ ○○○○○
Security _____ ○○○○○
Stealth _____ ○○○○○
Survival _____ ○○○○○

Knowledges
Computer _____ ○○○○○
Enigmas _____ ●●●○○
Gremayre _____ ●●●○○
Investigation _____ ○○○○○
Law _____ ○○○○○
Linguistics _____ ○○○○○
Lore _____ ●○○○○
Medicine _____ ○○○○○
Politics _____ ●●○○○
Science _____ ○○○○○

Advantages

Backgrounds
Contacts ●○○○○
Dreamers ●○○○○
Remembrance ●○○○○
Resources ●●○○○
_____ ○○○○○

Arts
Soothsay ●●○○○
Sovereign ●○○○○
_____ ○○○○○
_____ ○○○○○
_____ ○○○○○

Realms
Actor ●●○○○
Fae ●●○○○
Scene ●○○○○
_____ ○○○○○
_____ ○○○○○

Other Traits
_____
_____
_____
_____
_____
_____
_____

Glamour
●●●●●○○○○○
□□□□□□□□□□

Willpower
●●●●●○○○○○
□□□□□□□□□□

Health

		Real	Chimerical
Bruised		□	□
Hurt	-1	□	□
Injured	-1	□	□
Wounded	-2	□	□
Mauled	-2	□	□
Crippled	-5	□	□
Incapacitated		□	□

Ravaging/Musing Threshold

Banality
●●●●●○○○○○
□□□□□□□□□□

Birthrights/Frailties

Experience: [ ]

Modern-Day Herbalist of House Daireann

Quote: *Something for an aching toe? I have just the thing. And if you believe the legends, it's also good for soothing a troubled heart.*

Background: After recovering from your initial shock at being stuck in a human body (and finding that commoners were a lot more powerful than you remember), you've come to like this new world. Right away, you saw that interest in herbalism, your old profession, hadn't faded with the years. Now there are shops and gardens all over the place! After selling a few pieces of jewelry, you were able to set up your own business, complete with a private greenhouse, herbal perfumes, soaps and medicines. People from all walks of life flock to get your wares, and what's more, they keep coming back. As in the old days, some folks still scoff, but you know your wares are particularly potent and effective. What only a few realize, though, is that in addition to your "public" stock you have a private stash as well, concocted from some rather nasty plants like belladonna, aconite, foxglove, hemlock, lobelia and so on. You ask no questions and hear no lies. If someone pays enough, you'll sell them one of your poisons and keep quiet. It's business, after all, and you aim to be the best source. And if anyone gives you trouble, well, that's what the hunting dagger and darts you always carry are for. Their tips have a strange, dark sheen about them, oddly enough, and no one's ever caused you difficulties more than once.

Roleplaying Hints: You're a good fighter, as are all members of your house, but your passion is for business and for the craft of herbalism. Be cordial and charming to those wanting your wares. Answer questions, give some free samples and encourage customers to buy for their friends. When those special clients come to ask about your more insidious potions, be forthright, cool and collected. It makes no difference to you how they use these items, but you try not to sell them to fools, either.

Equipment: Mortar and pestle, glass jars, storage bags, scissors, gardening tools.

Book of Lost Houses: The Second Coming

Name: _____ Court: *Unseelie* Seeming: *Wilder*
Player: _____ Legacies: *Outlaw/Squire* Kith: *Sidhe*
Chronicle: _____ House: *Daireann* Motley: _____

Attributes

Physical
Strength _____ ●●○○○
Dexterity _____ ●●●○○
Stamina _____ ●●○○○

Social
Charisma _____ ●●●○○
Manipulation _____ ●●●○○
Appearance _____ ●●●●○

Mental
Perception _____ ●●●○○
Intelligence _____ ●●●○○
Wits _____ ●●●●○

Abilities

Talents
Alertness _____ ●○○○○
Athletics _____ ●○○○○
Brawl _____ ●○○○○
Dodge _____ ●○○○○
Empathy _____ ●●○○○
Intimidation _____ ○○○○○
Kenning _____ ●●○○○
Persuasion _____ ○○○○○
Streetwise _____ ●●○○○
Subterfuge _____ ●●●○○

Skills
Crafts _____ ●●●○○
Drive _____ ●○○○○
Etiquette _____ ●○○○○
Firearms _____ ○○○○○
Leadership _____ ○○○○○
Melee _____ ●●○○○
Performance _____ ○○○○○
Security _____ ○○○○○
Stealth _____ ●●○○○
Survival _____ ●○○○○

Knowledges
Computer _____ ○○○○○
Enigmas _____ ●○○○○
Gremayre _____ ○○○○○
Investigation _____ ○○○○○
Law _____ ○○○○○
Linguistics _____ ○○○○○
Lore _____ ○○○○○
Medicine _____ ●○○○○
Politics _____ ○○○○○
Science *(Herbalism)* ●●●●○

Advantages

Backgrounds
Contacts _____ ●○○○○
Remembrance ____ ●●●○○
Resources _____ ●●○○○
_____ ○○○○○
_____ ○○○○○

Arts
Primal _____ ●●○○○
Sovereign _____ ●●○○○
Wayfare _____ ●●○○○
_____ ○○○○○
_____ ○○○○○

Realms
Actor _____ ●●○○○
Fae _____ ●●○○○
Prop _____ ●○○○○
_____ ○○○○○
_____ ○○○○○

Other Traits
_____
_____
_____
_____
_____
_____

Glamour
●●●●○○○○○○
☐☐☐☐☐☐☐☐☐☐

Willpower
●●●○○○○○○○
☐☐☐☐☐☐☐☐☐☐

Health

		Real	Chimerical
Bruised		☐	☐
Hurt	-1	☐	☐
Injured	-1	☐	☐
Wounded	-2	☐	☐
Mauled	-2	☐	☐
Crippled	-5	☐	☐
Incapacitated		☐	☐

Ravaging/Musing Threshold

Banality
●●●○○○○○○○
☐☐☐☐☐☐☐☐☐☐

Birthrights/Frailties

Experience: ☐

Opportunist of House Varich

Quote: *I want it all, I want it now . . . and you will gladly help me get it.*

Background: When the way out of Arcadia opened up, you were ready to move. Patterns of possibility pointed you to this world where so much has changed, and yet, so much is the same. You found yourself in the body of a youth wandering through a museum filled with great treasures and opportunities. Your outer clothing was rough, but you could feel the weight of a heavy knife in a sheath along your back and luxurious cashmere against your skin. Faint memories, echoes of the mind and spirit of the one you displaced, told you that you were a messenger working for the *mafiya*, a *reketiry* (racketeer) living in luxury on anything that could turn one ruble into more. Patterns of profit, of favors asked and answered, all spread out as an intricate piece of artwork in your head. You were there to meet one of the museum curators; she was willing to turn a profit by "lending" some of the ancient riches the government kept on display. By the time you left, not only had you made a secondary deal, but you were also richer by one amber farseeing sphere, a treasure lost to your house.

Although you have not been here long, your mundane superiors now look at you with new eyes. They sense your natural superiority and have given you more responsibility each day. You know that soon you will be their master. The patterns are all there, waiting to be traced and shifted to acknowledge you as part of modern nobility. Manipulation is your joy and your art, and the sense of danger in this dark, Banal world only adds to your exhilaration. Soon your house will once again rule the peasants of this land and its spirits, and you are one of those best suited to the task.

Roleplaying Hints: Smile mysteriously when anyone asks you about your business. Show your elegance and style, remembering all the while that others may envy you and turn against you. Do not fear letting them know you may be useful if respected, dangerous if betrayed. Watch for patterns and relationships and see how easily they can be manipulated and changed to suit your needs. Be willing to lay down your life for your own sense of honor and for your house, but only as a last resort. You are intelligent enough to figure out ways around any thorny problems with honor.

Equipment: Chimerical weapon, treasure, elegant contraband clothing.

Book of Lost Houses: The Second Coming

Name: _____ Court: *Unseelie* Seeming: *Wilder*
Player: _____ Legacies: *Outlaw/Paladin* Kith: *Sidhe*
Chronicle: _____ House: *Varich* Motley: _____

Attributes

Physical
Strength _____ ●●○○○
Dexterity _____ ●●○○○
Stamina _____ ●●○○○

Social
Charisma _____ ●●○○○
Manipulation _____ ●●●●●
Appearance _____ ●●●●○

Mental
Perception _____ ●●●○○
Intelligence _____ ●●●○○
Wits _____ ●●●○○

Abilities

Talents
Alertness _____ ○○○○○
Athletics _____ ○○○○○
Brawl _____ ●○○○○
Dodge _____ ●○○○○
Empathy _____ ●○○○○
Intimidation _____ ●●○○○
Kenning _____ ●●○○○
Persuasion _____ ●●●○○
Streetwise _____ ●○○○○
Subterfuge _____ ●●○○○

Skills
Crafts _____ ○○○○○
Drive _____ ○○○○○
Etiquette _____ ●○○○○
Firearms _____ ○○○○○
Leadership _____ ●●○○○
Melee _____ ●●○○○
Performance _____ ○○○○○
Security _____ ○○○○○
Stealth _____ ●○○○○
Survival _____ ○○○○○

Knowledges
Computer _____ ○○○○○
Enigmas _____ ●●○○○
Gremayre _____ ○○○○○
Investigation _____ ○○○○○
Law _____ ●○○○○
Linguistics _____ ●●○○○
Lore _____ ●●○○○
Medicine _____ ○○○○○
Politics _____ ●●○○○
Science _____ ○○○○○

Advantages

Backgrounds
Chimera (Weapon) ●●○○○
Contacts ●●○○○
Resources ●●○○○
Treasures ●○○○○
_____ ___ ○○○○○

Arts
Legerdemain ●●○○○
Sovereign ●○○○○
Wayfare ●○○○○
_____ ○○○○○
_____ ○○○○○

Realms
Actor ●●○○○
Fae ●●○○○
Scene ●○○○○
_____ ○○○○○
_____ ○○○○○

Other Traits
_____
_____
_____
_____
_____
_____
_____

Glamour
●●●●○○○○○○
□□□□□□□□□□

Willpower
●●●○○○○○○○
□□□□□□□□□□

Health

	Real	Chimerical
Bruised	□	□
Hurt -1	□	□
Injured -1	□	□
Wounded -2	□	□
Mauled -2	□	□
Crippled -5	□	□
Incapacitated	□	□

Ravaging/Musing Threshold

Banality
●●●○○○○○○○
□□□□□□□□□□

Birthrights/Frailties

Experience: [ ]

Dream Alienist of House Scathach

Quote: *In temperate conditions, if a body is warm but not yet stiff, the victim has been dead less than 3 hours. If he is cold and stiff, it's been somewhere between 8 and 36 hours. After about two days the body becomes warm again as putrefaction sets in. How long does it take a dream to decay?*

Background: *Never* mix your drinks. You remember a time when magic and law enforcement went well together. You played at cops and robbers, Sherlock Holmes hot on the trail of the nefarious Moriarty—magic. The real world of law enforcement, however, was far more ugly, mad and trivial. You drank to get away from the horrors of your job and buried yourself in your work to avoid looking at yourself too closely in the mirror. And for a long time the magic went away. For fifteen years as a "profiler" for the FBI, yours was a corner of the world shared only by the most violent killers and the mad few who pursued them. You thought you had seen it all; you were wrong.

The case was a sick one, even by the high standards set by your profession. The press had dubbed the killer the "Nappy Napper," and his victims were children, young ones. They disappeared from rich and poor neighborhoods alike, from under the eyes of watchful guardians and from locked houses without a trace. Well, that is not quite true; there were the bodies. It was a cold night in a rundown mill town on the edge of nowhere. You arrived while the photographers were still snapping away and the detectives still joking over their coffee. The missing boy, four-year-old Charlie Lane, still clutched a teddy in his small hands. A rip in Teddy's side leaked cotton stuffing in sickening counterpoint to the blood congealing around the child's tiny, crumpled form. Cuts, bruise marks, skin lividity—a dead body always has a tale to tell, but this one's story was completely new. You thought you had seen it all, but nothing could have prepared you for when Teddy stood up, shook his head and slowly, unsteadily began to walk toward you. . . .

Roleplaying Hints: From Miami to Richmond to St. Claire, you followed the killer's footprints in the sands of Fate, each chimerical step growing clearer on the way. The trail that brought you to a supernatural killer also led you back to your true self; the magic was coming back. It didn't hurt that you had stopped drinking the night you met Teddy. You weren't the only one on the killer's trail. The Bureau's Special Affairs Division, the department involved in monitoring "paranormal" activities, thought you might have a knack for the job; they don't know the half of it.

You have reestablished your old contacts with House Scathach, finding new purpose in your profession. One thing that has always struck you about the "science" of criminal psychiatry is that it is nine parts art and only one part science. Pathology, serology, dactyloscopy and toxicology, each are precise, if not infallible, sciences. Not so the job of the profiler, to use the current job description. You have always preferred the old title *alienist*. Getting into the mind of a killer, you can use no other word to describe it.

Equipment: Camera, notebook, FBI badge, agency issued firearm, pocket tape recorder.

CHRIS HOWARD '01

Book of Lost Houses: The Second Coming

Name: _____
Player: _____
Chronicle: _____

Court: *Seelie*
Legacies: *Sage/Fatalist*
House: *Scathach*

Seeming: *Grump*
Kith: *Sidhe*
Motley: _____

Attributes

Physical
Strength _____ ●●○○○
Dexterity _____ ●●●○○
Stamina _____ ●●●○○

Social
Charisma _____ ●●○○○
Manipulation _____ ●●●○○
Appearance _____ ●●●●○

Mental
Perception _____ ●●●●●
Intelligence _____ ●●●○○
Wits _____ ●●●○○

Abilities

Talents
Alertness _____ ●●○○○
Athletics _____ ○○○○○
Brawl _____ ○○○○○
Dodge _____ ○○○○○
Empathy _____ ●●●○○
Intimidation _____ ○○○○○
Kenning _____ ●●○○○
Persuasion _____ ○○○○○
Streetwise _____ ○○○○○
Subterfuge _____ ○○○○○

Skills
Crafts _____ ○○○○○
Drive _____ ●○○○○
Etiquette _____ ●●○○○
Firearms _____ ●●●○○
Leadership _____ ●●○○○
Melee _____ ●●○○○
Performance _____ ○○○○○
Security _____ ●●○○○
Stealth _____ ●●○○○
Survival _____ ○○○○○

Knowledges
Computer _____ ●●○○○
Enigmas _____ ●●○○○
Gremayre _____ ●●●○○
Investigation _____ ●●●●○
Law _____ ●●●○○
Linguistics _____ ○○○○○
Lore _____ ●●○○○
Medicine _____ ○○○○○
Politics _____ ○○○○○
Science _____ ●●○○○

Advantages

Backgrounds
Mastery _____ ●●○○○
Resources _____ ●●○○○
"Title" _____ ●●○○○
(FBI Veteran, Special Affairs) ○○○○○
_____ ○○○○○

Arts
Chicanery _____ ●●○○○
Soothsay _____ ●●○○○
_____ ○○○○○
_____ ○○○○○
_____ ○○○○○

Realms
Actor _____ ●●●○○
Fae _____ ●○○○○
Scene _____ ●○○○○
_____ ○○○○○
_____ ○○○○○

Other Traits
Oracle   *4pt Merit*
Echoes   *3pt Flaw*
_____
_____
_____
_____

Glamour
●●●○○○○○○○
☐☐☐☐☐☐☐☐☐☐

Willpower
●●●●●○○○○○
☐☐☐☐☐☐☐☐☐☐

Health

	Real	Chimerical
Bruised	☐	☐
Hurt −1	☐	☐
Injured −1	☐	☐
Wounded −2	☐	☐
Mauled −2	☐	☐
Crippled −5	☐	☐
Incapacitated	☐	☐

Ravaging/Musing Threshold

Banality
●●●●○○○○○○
☐☐☐☐☐☐☐☐☐☐

Birthrights/Frailties

Experience: ☐

	CHANGELING The Dreaming™	MAGE THE SORCERERS CRUSADE	
APRIL	THE BOOK OF LOST HOUSES	THE ORDER OF REASON	
JUNE	KITHBOOK: ESHU		
JULY			
AUGUST		WITCHES AND PAGANS	
SEPTEMBER		HOSTS OF HEAVEN	
OCTOBER	THE BOOK OF GLAMOUR		
NOVEMBER		LANDS OF MYSTERY: ARABIA, INDIA & CATHAY	
DECEMBER			

COMING THIS YEAR FROM ARTHAUS
AND RISING FROM THE GRAVE THIS FALL...

	A	**TRINITY**
		HOPE · SACRIFICE · UNITY
	ABERRANT: Underworld	Terre Verde
	ABERRANT: Brainwaves	
	ABERRANT: Nexus	
	ABERRANT: Brute Force	Asia Ascendant

COMING
NEXT
FOR
CHANGELING-
KITHBOOK:
Eshu